FreeCAD 0.20

Basics Tutorial

Tutorial Books

Send us an email to <u>freecadtuts@gmail.com</u> to get resource files

Contents

Scope of this book...ix

Chapter 1: Getting Started with FreeCAD...1

Starting FreeCAD...2

Workbenches in FreeCAD..3

User Interface...4

Menu bar..4

Toolbar...4

Status bar...14

Dialog..14

Navigation Styles..15

Background...15

Chapter 2: Part Modeling Basics...18

TUTORIAL 1...18

Starting a New Part File...18

Starting a Sketch..12

Adding Constraints..12

Creating the Base Feature..13

Adding a Pad Feature...15

Filleting the Corners...16

Changing the View Orientation...17

Rotating and Moving the Part..17

Shelling the model...18

Saving the Part...18

TUTORIAL 2...19

Starting a New File..19

Sketching for the Pad Feature..19

Creating the Cut Feature..21

Chapter 3: Assembly Basics..27

TUTORIAL 1...27

Starting a New Assembly File..27

Inserting the Base Component..27

Adding the second component..28

Applying Constraints..28

Chapter 4: Sketching **34**

Creating Polylines 34

Creating Polygons 35

Creating a Slot.. 35

Constraints 36

Constrain Coincident 36

Constrain horizontally 36

Constrain Vertically 36

Constrain tangent 36

Constrain Parallel 36

Constrain Perpendicular.. 37

Auto Constraints 37

Deleting Constraints 37

Constrain Lock 38

Constrain Block 38

Hiding Constraints 39

Create B-Spline 39

Create periodic B-spline 39

Ellipses.. 39

Extend Edge 40

Trim Edge 41

Constrain point onto object.. 41

Toggle Construction geometry 42

TUTORIAL 1 42

Chapter 5: Additional Modeling Tools **48**

TUTORIAL 1 48

Creating the First Feature 48

Creating the Pocket feature 50

Creating a Polar Pattern.. 53

Adding the Pad feature.. 53

Creating a Counterbore Hole 54

Creating Threaded holes.. 55

Creating Chamfers... 56

TUTORIAL 2 57

Creating the first feature..57

Creating the Shell feature..58

Creating the Third feature..58

Creating the Rib Feature..60

Creating a Pocket Feature..62

TUTORIAL 3..62

Creating the Profile..62

Creating the Helix..63

Creating the Sweep..63

TUTORIAL 4..64

Creating the Loft feature..64

Creating the Extruded feature..68

Creating Fillets...69

Shelling the Model...69

Adding Threads..70

TUTORIAL 5..72

Creating the First feature..72

Creating the Pocket Feature..74

TUTORIAL 6..75

Constructing a cylindrical shell...75

Adding a Slot...76

Constructing the Linear and Circular patterns using the MultiTransform tool....................................77

TUTORIAL 7..77

Constructing the Groove feature..78

TUTORIAL 8..80

Creating the Base Feature...80

Creating the Pocket Features..81

Creating the Pocket Feature on the left side...86

Creating the Angled Cut..87

Creating the Pocket feature on the left...89

Creating the Pocket feature on the right...90

Adding the Pad Features...93

TUTORIAL 9..97

Creating the first feature..97

Creating the Shell feature 99

Creating the Flanges 100

TUTORIAL 10 105

Creating the first feature 105

Creating the Second feature 106

Creating the third feature 111

Creating the fourth feature 113

Creating Holes 115

Creating the Pocket feature 116

TUTORIAL 11 117

Creating the Base 117

Creating the Rib 119

Creating the Third feature 122

Creating the Pocket Feature 125

TUTORIAL 12 126

TUTORIAL 13 129

Creating Configuration Table 131

Chapter 6: Creating Drawings **133**

TUTORIAL 1 133

Starting a New Drawing File 133

Generating the Base View 135

Generating the Section View 135

Creating the Detailed View 136

Adding Dimensions 136

Populating the Title Block 139

Chapter 7: Sheet Metal Modeling **140**

TUTORIAL 1 140

Creating the Base Feature 140

Creating the flange 141

Extending a face 143

Creating the Pockets 145

Creating the Flat Pattern 147

Creating 2D Drawing of the sheet metal part 148

TUTORIAL 2 149

Creating the Base Feature 149

Creating Thickness feature 151

TUTORIAL 3 152

Creating the Base Feature 152

Creating the flange 154

Creating Extruded Cuts 155

TUTORIAL 4 156

Adding Corner Reliefs 157

Fold a wall using a Sketch 157

TUTORIAL 5 160

Ripping the Edges of the Model 160

Making Bends 161

Adding Corner Relief 162

Making a Forming in Wall 163

Chapter 8: CAM Overview **166**

TUTORIAL 1 166

Creating the Job 166

Adding Tools to the Job 167

Creating the Facing Operation 169

Creating the Pocket Operation 171

Creating the Drill Operation 172

Drilling Holes using the Helix Operation 172

Creating the Contour Operation 173

Post Processing 174

INTRODUCTION

FreeCAD, as a topic of learning, is very vast and has a broad scope. It is a package of many workbenches delivering exceptional value to enterprises. It offers a set of tools, which are easy-to-use to design, document, and simulate 3D models. Using this software, you can design your products free of cost.

This book provides a step-by-step approach for users to learn FreeCAD. It is aimed at those with no previous experience with FreeCAD. The user is guided by starting a FreeCAD session to creating parts, assemblies, and drawings. Each chapter has components explained with the help of real-world models.

Scope of this book

This book is written for students and engineers who are interested to learn FreeCAD for designing mechanical components and assemblies, and then create drawings.

This book provides a step-by-step approach to learning FreeCAD. The topics include Getting Started with FreeCAD, Basic Part Modeling, Creating Assemblies, Additional Modeling Tools, and Creating Drawings.

Chapter 1 introduces FreeCAD. The user interface and terminology are discussed in this chapter.

Chapter 2 takes you through the creation of your first FreeCAD model. You create simple parts.

Chapter 3 teaches you to create assemblies. It explains the Top-down and Bottom-up approaches for designing an assembly. You create an assembly using the Bottom-up approach.

Chapter 4: In this chapter, you learn the sketching tools.

Chapter 5: In this chapter, you learn additional modeling tools to create complex models.

Chapter 6 teaches you to create drawings of the models created in the earlier chapters.

Chapter 7 teaches you to create a sheet metal model.

Chapter 1: Getting Started with FreeCAD

This tutorial book brings in the most commonly used features of FreeCAD.

In this chapter, you will:

- Understand the FreeCAD terminology
- Start a new file
- Understand the User Interface
- Understand different workbenches in FreeCAD

In FreeCAD, you create 3D parts and use them to create 2D drawings and 3D assemblies.

FreeCAD is Feature Based. Features are shapes that are combined to build a part. You can modify these shapes individually.

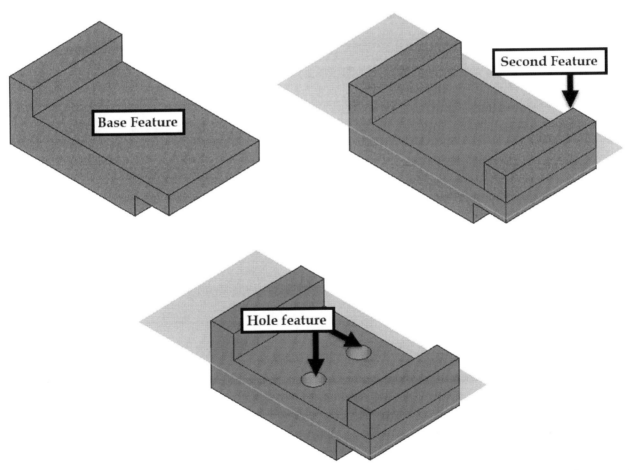

Most of the features are sketch-based. A sketch is a 2D profile and can be extruded, revolved, or swept along a path to create features.

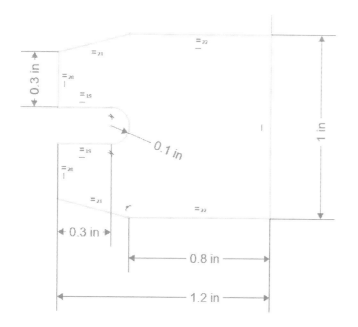

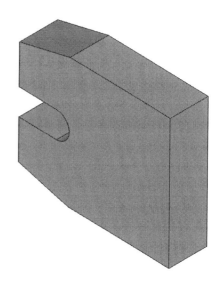

FreeCAD is parametric. You can specify standard parameters between the elements. Changing these parameters changes the size and shape of the part. For example, see the design of the body of a flange before and after modifying the parameters of its features.

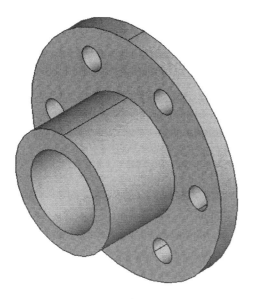

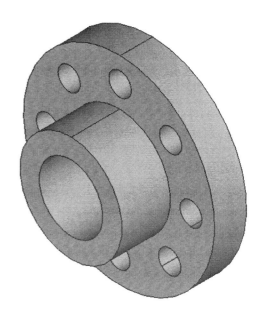

Starting FreeCAD

- Click the Windows icon on the taskbar.
- Click **F > FreeCAD 0.20 > FreeCAD**.
- On the ribbon, click **File > New** to start a new part file.

Notice these essential features of the FreeCAD window.

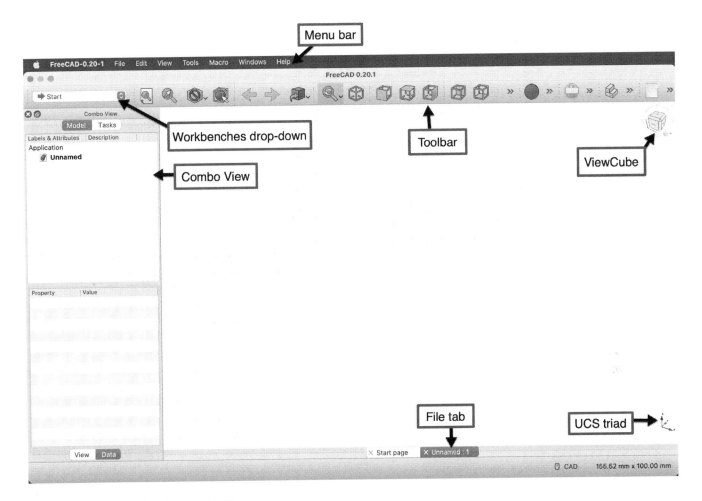

Workbenches in FreeCAD

A workbench is a set of tools and environments that can be used to create parts, assemblies, drawings, and so on. There are many workbenches available in FreeCAD. You can activate different workbenches by using the **Workbenches** drop-down located on the top-left corner.

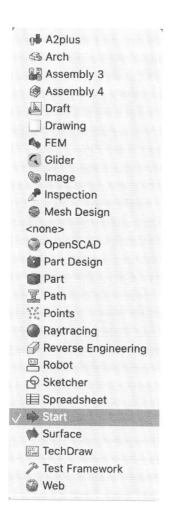

User Interface

Various components of the user interface are discussed next.

Menu bar

The menu bar is located at the top of the window. It has various options (menu titles). When you click on a menu title, a drop-down appears. Select an option from this drop-down.

File Menu

The **File Menu** appears when you click on the **File** option located at the top left corner of the window. This menu contains the options to open, print, export, save, and close a file.

Toolbar

A toolbar is a set of tools, which help you to perform various operations. Various toolbars available in different workbenches are given next.

Start Toolbars		
Workbench ➡ Start		This toolbar has a drop-down to change the workbench.
Macro		This toolbar has tools to create and execute macros.
File		This toolbar has tools to create, open, and save files. You can also print, cut, copy, paste, undo, redo, recompute, and seek help.
View		This toolbar has tools to manipulate the view of the model.
Structure		It has tools to create or open part files.
Navigation		It has tools to open a website in

	FreeCAD.
Sketcher Toolbars	
Sketcher	This toolbar has tools to start or exit a sketch.
Sketcher geometries	This toolbar has tools to create sketch elements.
Sketcher constraints	This toolbar has tools to apply constraints between sketch elements.
Sketcher B-spline tools	This toolbar has tools to create and edit B-splines.
Sketcher Virtual Space	This toolbar helps you to hide or show constraints.

Sketch Tools 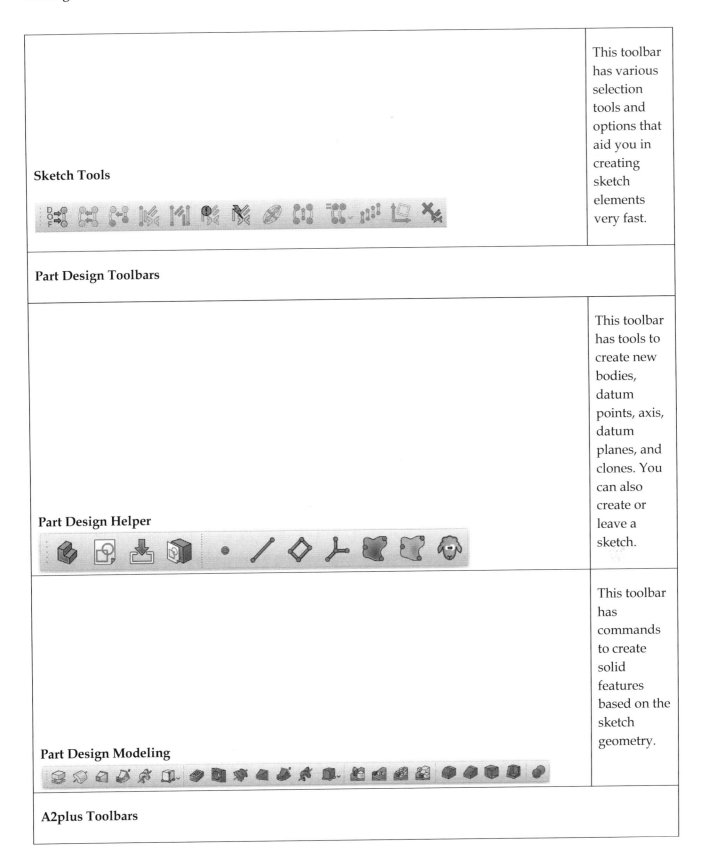	This toolbar has various selection tools and options that aid you in creating sketch elements very fast.
Part Design Toolbars	
Part Design Helper	This toolbar has tools to create new bodies, datum points, axis, datum planes, and clones. You can also create or leave a sketch.
Part Design Modeling	This toolbar has commands to create solid features based on the sketch geometry.
A2plus Toolbars	

A2p_Part	This toolbar has tools to create components or insert existing components into an assembly.
A2p_Constraint	This toolbar also has tools to apply constraints between components.
A2p_Solver	This toolbar has tools to change the direction of the constraints and solve constraints.
A2p_View	This toolbar has tools to change the display of the assembly.
TechDraw Toolbars	
TechDraw Views	This toolbar has tools to generate standard views of a

	3D geometry.
TechDraw Clips	It has tools to add or remove clips to the drawing sheet.
TechDraw Pages	The tools on this toolbar help you to add a new page.
TechDraw Dimensions	The tools on this toolbar help you to add dimensions to the drawing views.
TechDraw File Access	This toolbar helps you to export the drawing page to the SVG or DXF format.
TechDraw Decoration	The tools on this toolbar help you to change the hatch patterns and insert images.

TechDraw Attributes	The tools on this toolbar help you to modify the attributes of the dimensions.
TechDraw Centerlines	The tools on this toolbar help you to add centerlines and centermarks to the drawing views.
TechDraw Extend Dimensions	The tools on this toolbar help you to additional types of dimensions to the drawing view such as chain dimensions, coordinate dimensions, chamfer dimensions, and so on.
Sheet Metal Toolbars	
Sheet Metal	The tools on this toolbar help you to create a

		sheetmetal model.
FEM Toolbars		
Model		It has tools to define materials and element geometry of the model.

Mechanical Constraints	It has tools to define mechanical constriants.
Thermal Constraints	It has tools to add thermal constraints.
Mesh	It has tools to mesh the model.
Fluid Constraints	It has tools to add fluid constraints.
Electronstatic Constraints	It has tools to add electrostatic constraints.
Solve	It has tools to perform the finite element analysis.
Results	It has tools display the results of finite element analysis.

Utilities		It has tools to clip and unclip faces.
Path Toolbars		
Project Setup		It has tools to create a job and export G-Code.
Tool Commands		It has tools to create and manage tools.
New Operations		It has tools to create machining operations.
Path Modification		It has tools to modify tool paths.

You can hide or show toolbars in the application window. To do this, click **View > Toolbars**, and then select the toolbar name from the list displayed.

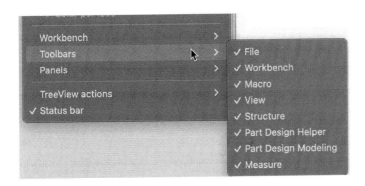

Status bar

The Status bar is available below the graphics window. It shows the action taken while using the commands.

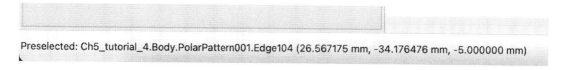

Preselected: Ch5_tutorial_4.Body.PolarPattern001.Edge104 (26.567175 mm, -34.176476 mm, -5.000000 mm)

Model tab

It contains the list of operations carried while constructing a part.

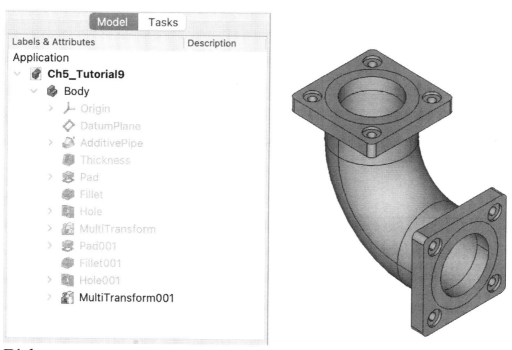

Dialog

When you click any tool in FreeCAD, the dialog related to it appears in the **Tasks** tab of the **Combo View** panel. A dialog has various options. The following figure shows various components of a dialog.

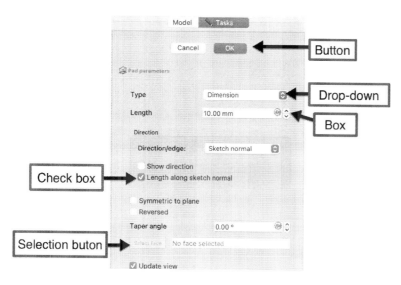

This book uses the default options on the dialog.

Navigation Styles

FreeCAD provides you with different types of mouse navigation styles: **OpenInventor**, **CAD**, **Revit**, **Blender**, **MayaGesture**, **TinkerCAD**, **Touchpad**, **Gesture**, and **OpenCascade**. You can select the desired navigation style from the drop-down located at the bottom right corner.

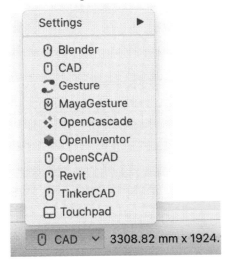

This book uses the CAD Navigation Style for your mouse. Select the **CAD** option from the **Navigation Styles** drop-down. Next, place the mouse cursor on the drop-down; the various mouse functions are displayed.

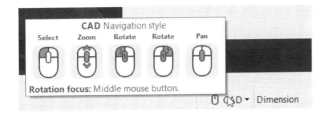

Background

To change the background color of the window, click **Edit > Preferences** on the Menu bar. On the **Preferences** dialog, click **Display** on the left side. Click the **Colors** tab and set the colors for various element types.

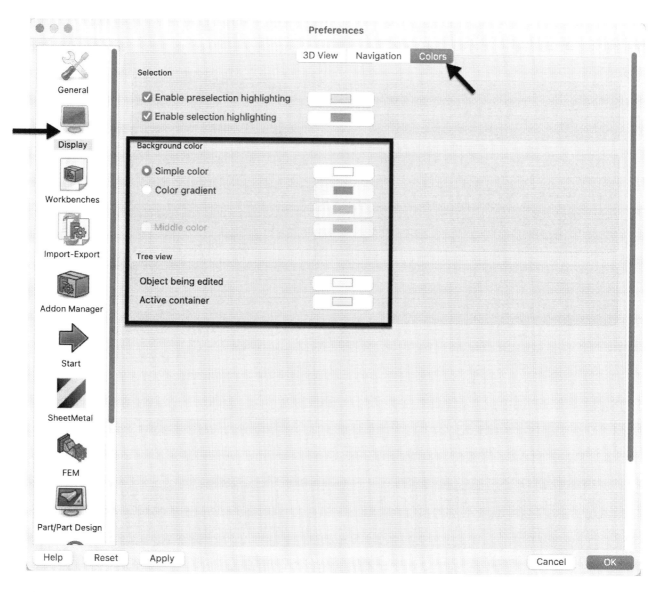

To change the color of sketch elements, click **Sketcher** on the left side, and then click the **Colors** tab. Next, change the **Sketch colors**. Click **OK** to apply the changes.

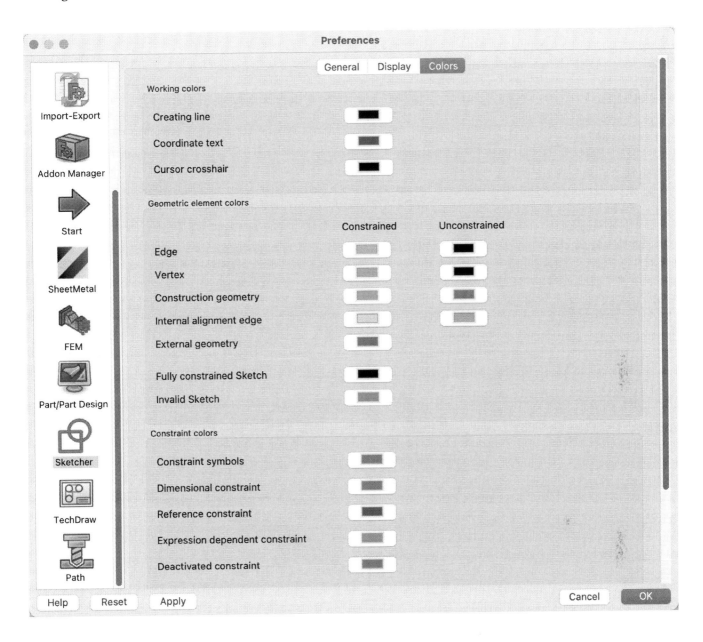

Chapter 2: Part Modeling Basics

This chapter takes you through the creation of your first FreeCAD model. You create simple parts:

In this chapter, you will:

- Create Sketches
- Create a base feature
- Add another feature to it
- Add fillets
- Shell the model
- Create Pocket features

TUTORIAL 1

This tutorial takes you through the creation of your first FreeCAD model.

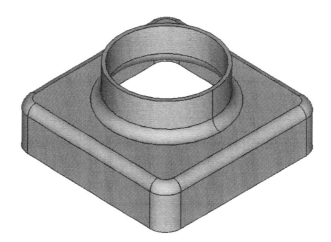

Starting a New Part File

1. To start a new part file, click **File > New** on the Menu Bar (or) click the **New** icon on the **File** toolbar.

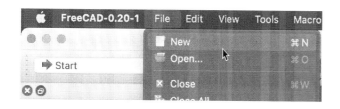

(or)

A new model window appears.

2. On the **Workbench** toolbar, select **Workbench** drop-down > **Part Design** (or) select **View > Workbench > Part Design** on the Menu bar.

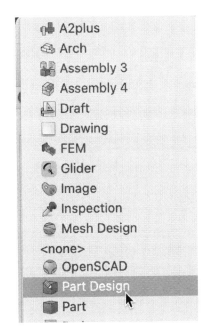

(or)

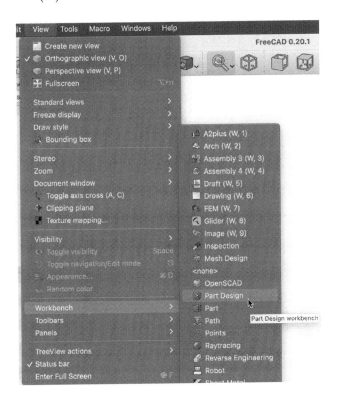

Starting a Sketch

1. To start a new sketch, click **Part Design Helper** toolbar > **Create New Sketch** (or) click **Sketch > Create Sketch** on the Menu bar.

2. Select the **XY_Plane**, and then click **OK**. The sketch starts.

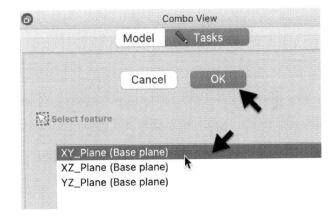

Notice that:

- The grid and sketch origin appear.
- The **Sketcher**, **Sketcher geometries**, **Sketcher constraints**, **Sketcher tools**, **Sketcher B-spline tools**, and **Sketcher virtual space** toolbars are displayed.
- "**Empty Sketch**" appears in the **Solver Messages** section in the **Combo View** panel.

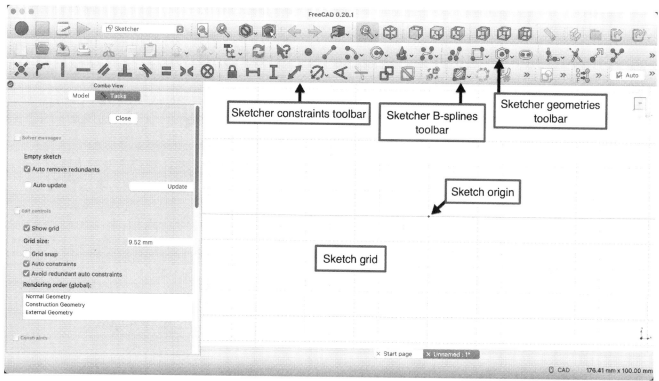

Before you begin sketching, make sure that your FreeCAD settings match the settings used in this tutorial.

3. Click **Edit > Preferences** on the Menu bar. The **Preferences** dialog box appears. If you are working on MacOS, then click **FreeCAD > Preferences** on the title bar.

4. On the **Preferences** dialog box, click the **General** option at the left side and then click the **Units** tab.

5. Select **User System > Standard (mm/kg/s/degree)**.

6. Type **2** in the **Number of decimal** box.

7. Click **OK**.

8. In the **Edit Controls** section of the **Tasks** tab of the **Combo View** panel, make sure that the **Show grid** checkbox is selected.

The first feature is an extruded feature from a sketched rectangular profile. You begin by sketching the rectangle.

9. On the **Sketcher geometries** toolbar, click the **Rectangle** icon (or) click **Sketch > Sketcher geometries > Create Rectangle**.

10. Move the cursor to the sketch origin located at the center of the graphics window, and then click on it.

11. Drag the cursor towards the top right corner, and then click to create a rectangle.

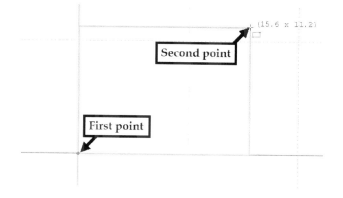

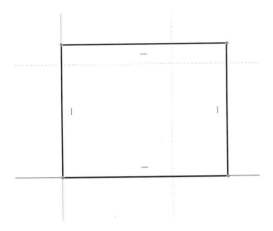

12. Press **ESC** to deactivate the tool.

Adding Constraints

In this section, you specify the size of the sketched rectangle by adding constraints. As you add constraints, the sketch can attain any one of the following states:

Fully Constrained sketch: In a fully constrained sketch, the positions of all the entities are fully described by constraints. In a fully constrained sketch, all the entities are a green color.

Under Constrained sketch: Additional constraints are needed to specify the geometry completely. In this state, you can drag the under constrained sketch entities to modify the sketch. An under constrained sketch entity is in black.

Redundant Constraints: Redundant constraints are unwanted constraints that you add to an already fully defined sketch. FreeCAD has a special option called **Auto remove redundants** to delete the unwanted constraints. By default, this option is selected on the Tasks tab of the Combo View panel. As a result, the redundant constraints are deleted automatically when you try to add them to a fully constrained sketch.

1. Click **Sketcher constraints** toolbar > **Constrain vertical distance** (or) click **Sketch > Sketcher constraints > Constrain vertical distance** on the menu bar.

2. Select the right vertical line of the rectangle.
3. Enter **100** in the **Length** box of the **Insert Length** dialog and click **OK**.
4. Click **Sketcher constraints** toolbar > **Constrain horizontal distance** (or) click **Sketch > Sketcher constraints > Constrain horizontal distance** on the menu bar.
5. Select the bottom horizontal line of the rectangle.
6. Enter **100** in the **Length** box of the **Insert Length** dialog and click the **OK** button.

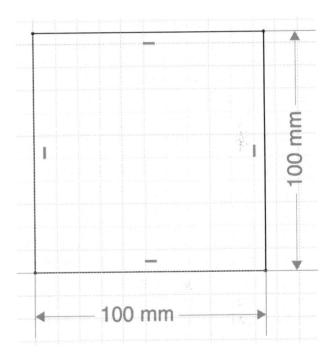

7. Press **Esc** to deactivate the **Constrain horizontal distance** tool.
8. To display the entire rectangle at full size and to center it in the graphics area, use one of the following methods:

   - Click **Fit All** on the **View** toolbar.

   - Click **View > Standard Views > Fit All** on the Menu bar.

9. Click **Close** on the **Combo View** panel.

10. Again, click **Fit All** on the **View** toolbar.

Creating the Base Feature

The first feature in any part is called a base feature. You now create this feature by extruding the sketched rectangle.

1. Click **Part Design Modeling** toolbar > **Pad** (or) click **Part Design > Pad** on the Menu bar.
2. Type-in 25 in the **Length** box available on the **Pad parameters** dialog on the **Combo View** panel.
3. Click **OK** on the **Combo View** panel to create the pad feature.

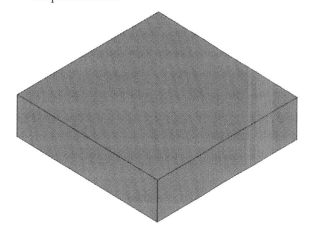

Notice the new feature, **Pad**, in the **Model** tab of the **Combo View** panel.

To magnify a model in the graphics area, you can use the zoom tools available on the **Zoom** submenu in the **View** menu of the Menu bar.

Click **Zoom In** to zoom into the model.

Click **Zoom Out** to zoom out of the model.

Click **Box Zoom**, and then drag the pointer to create a rectangle; the area in the rectangle zooms to fill the window.

The **View** toolbar has two more zoom tools: **Fit All** and **Fit Selection**.

Click **Fit All** to display the full part size in the current window.

Click on a vertex, an edge, or a feature, and then click **Fit Selection** ; the selected item zooms to fill the window.

13

To display the part in different draw styles, select the options in the **Draw Style** drop-down on the **View** toolbar.

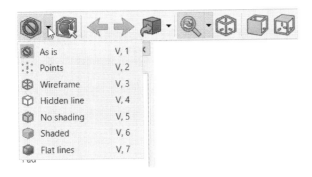

Normal Mode

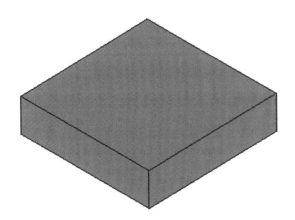

Flat lines

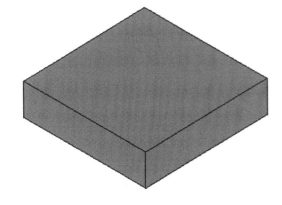

Shaded

Wireframe

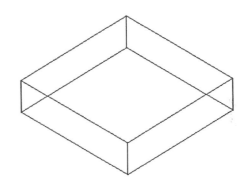

Points

Hidden Line

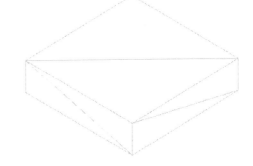

No Shading

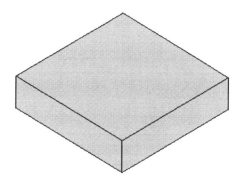

The default draw style for parts and assemblies is **Normal Mode**. You may change the draw style whenever you want.

Adding a Pad Feature

To create additional features on the part, you need to draw sketches on the model faces or planes, and then extrude them.

1. Click on the top face of the first feature.

2. Click **Create Sketch** on the **Face tools** section of the **Tasks** tab. A new sketch is started.

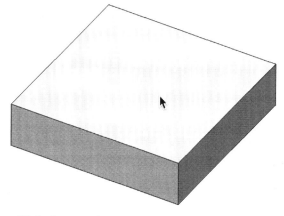

3. On the **Sketcher geometries** toolbar, click **Circle** drop-down > **Center and rim point.**

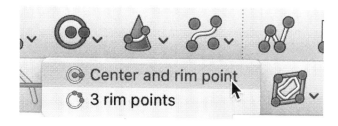

4. Click to specify the center point of the circle.
5. Move the pointer outward and click to create the circle.

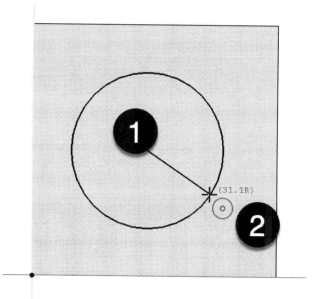

6. On the **Sketcher constraints** toolbar, click the **Constrain distance** icon.
7. Select the center point of the circle.
8. Select the horizontal axis of the sketch.
9. Type **50** in the **Length** box of the **Insert Length** dialog.
10. Click **OK**.

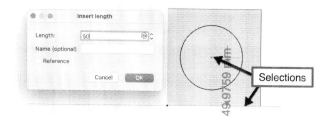

11. Select the center point of the circle and the vertical axis of the sketch.

12. Type **50** in the **Length** box and click **OK**.

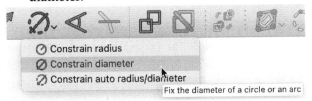

13. On the **Sketcher constraints** toolbar, click the **Constrain diameter** drop-down > **Constrain diameter**.

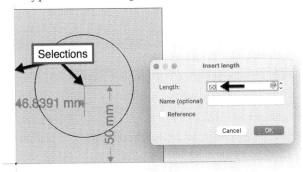

14. Select the circle and type **30** in the **Radius** box of the **Change Radius** dialog.

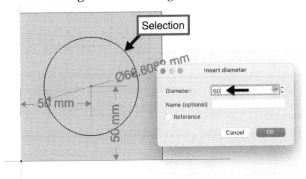

15. Click **OK**.

16. On the **Sketcher** toolbar, click the **Leave Sketch** icon.

17. On the **Part Design Modeling** toolbar, click the **Pad**  icon.

18. Type **20** in the **Length** box of the **Pad Parameters** dialog.

19. Click **OK**.

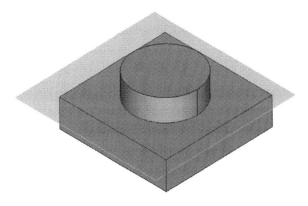

Filleting the Corners

The **Fillet** tool allows you to fillet the corners of the model.

1. On the **View** toolbar, select **Draw style > Wireframe**.

2. Press and hold the Ctrl key (Command key for MacOS users) and select the vertical edges of the model, as shown.

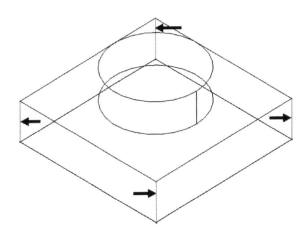

16

3. On the **Part Design Modeling** toolbar, click the **Fillet** icon.
4. Type **10** in the **Radius** box.
5. Click **OK**.
6. On the **View** toolbar, select **Draw style > Flat lines** .
7. Click on the horizontal face of the model, as shown.

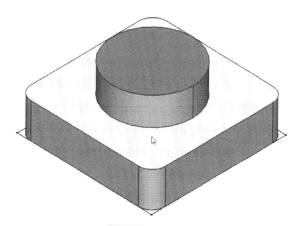

8. Click the **Fillet** icon on the **Part Design Modeling** toolbar.
9. Type **5** in the **Radius** box and click **OK**.

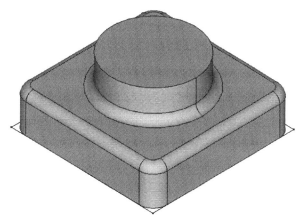

Changing the View Orientation

You can use the icons available on the **View** toolbar to change the view orientation of the sketch, part, or assembly.

 Front

 Top

  Right

  Rear

  Bottom

  Left

  Isometric

The default planes of the part corresponding to the standard views are as follows:

- **XZ Plane - Front** or **Back**
- **YZ Plane - Top** or **Bottom**
- **XY Plane - Right** or **Left**

Rotating and Moving the Part

In addition to standard views, you can view the model from different angles by rotating them. By doing so, you can select the hidden faces and edges easily.

To rotate the part, use one of the following methods:

- On the Menu bar, click **View > Standard Views > Rotate Left** to rotate the model towards left.

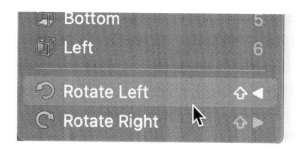

- On the Menu bar, click **Views > Standard Views > Rotate Right** to rotate the model towards the right.
- Press and hold the middle and the right mouse buttons. Next, drag the cursor to rotate the model.
- To rotate the part in 90° increments, press and hold the **Shift** key and use the arrow keys.

To move the part view, use one of the following methods:

- Press and hold the middle mouse button and drag the cursor.
- Press and hold the **Alt** or **Ctrl** key (**Command** key for Mac users) and use the arrow keys to move the view up, down, left, or right.

Shelling the model

The **Thickness** tool allows you to shell the model.

1. Press and hold the middle and right mouse buttons.
2. Drag the cursor upward to display the bottom face.
3. Click on the bottom face.

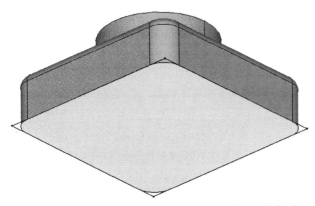

4. On the **Part Design Modeling** toolbar, click the **Thickness** icon.
5. In the **Thickness Parameters** dialog, select **Mode > Skin**.
6. Select **Join Type > Intersection**.
7. Type **2** in the **Thickness** box.
8. Check the **Make thickness inwards** option.
9. On the **View** toolbar, click the **Isometric** icon.

10. On the **Thickness parameters** dialog, click the **Add face** button.
11. Select the top face of the second feature.

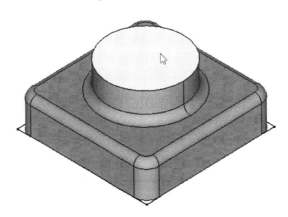

12. Click **OK**.

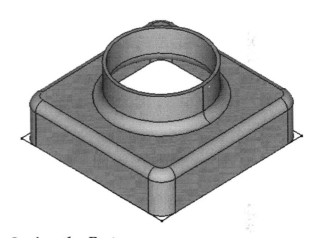

Saving the Part

1. Click **File > Save** on the Menu bar.
2. On the **Save As** dialog, type-in **Tutorial1** in the **File name** box.
3. Click **Save** to save the file.
4. Click **File > Close**.

Note:
*.FCStd is the file extension for all the files that you create in FreeCAD.

TUTORIAL 2

In this tutorial, you create the part shown below.

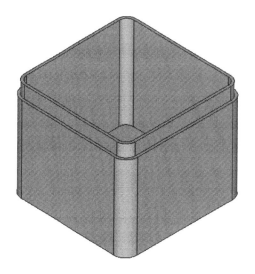

Starting a New File

1. On the Menu bar, click **File > New**.
2. Select **Part Design** from the **Workbench** drop-down.

Sketching for the Pad Feature

1. Click **Create Sketch** 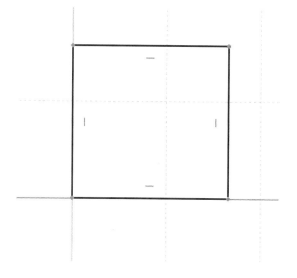 icon on the **Part Design Helper** toolbar.
2. Select the XY plane.
3. Click **OK**.
4. Click **Rectangle** on the **Sketcher geometries** toolbar.
5. Create a rectangle, shown in the figure.

6. Add vertical and horizontal distance constraints to the rectangle, as shown.

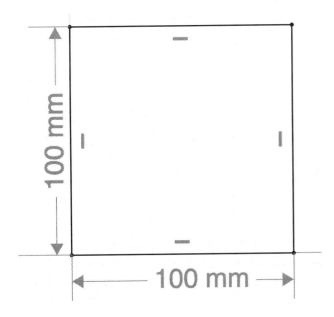

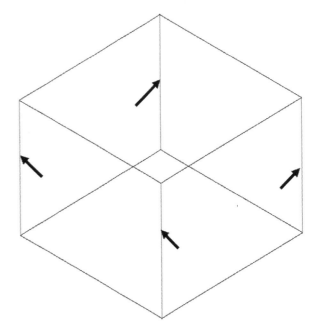

7. Click the **Leave Sketch** 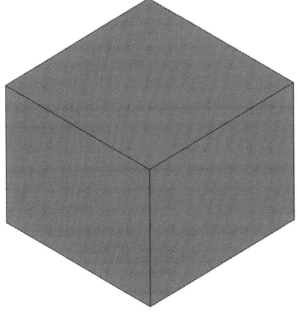 icon on the **Sketcher** toolbar.

8. Click **Pad** on the **Create** panel.

9. Type **80** in the **Length** box and click **OK**.

12. On the **Part Design Modeling** toolbar, click the **Fillet** icon.
13. Type 10 in the **Radius** box.
14. Click **OK**.
15. On the **View** toolbar, select **Draw Style > Flat lines**.

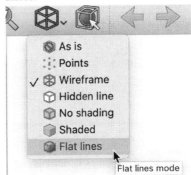

16. Click on the top face of the model.
17. Click the **Thickness** icon on the **Part Design Modeling** toolbar.
18. Type 4 in the **Thickness** box.
19. Select **Join Type > Intersection**.
20. Check the **Make thickness inwards** option.
21. Click **OK**.

10. Select **Draw Style > Wireframe** on the **View** toolbar.
11. Press and hold the Ctrl key (**Command** key for Mac users) and select the vertical edges.

20

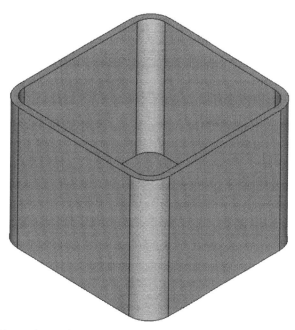

Creating the Cut Feature

1. Click on the top face of the first feature.

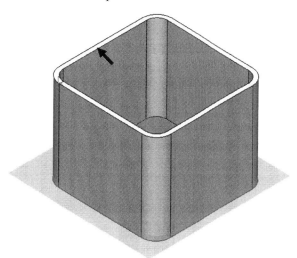

2. Click **Create Sketch** on the **Face tools** section of the **Tasks** tab. A new sketch is started.

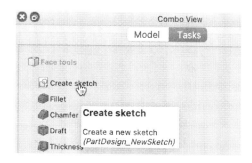

3. Click the **External geometry** icon on the **Sketcher geometries** toolbar.
4. Click on the inner edges of the model.

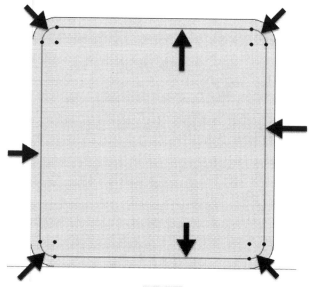

5. Click the **Rectangle** icon on the **Sketcher geometries** toolbar.
6. Create a rectangle, as shown.

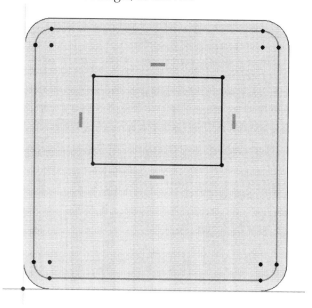

7. Click the **Create fillet** icon on the **Sketcher geometries** toolbar.
8. Click on the left vertical and the top horizontal line.

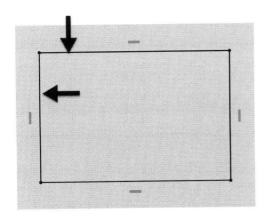

A fillet is created at the corner.

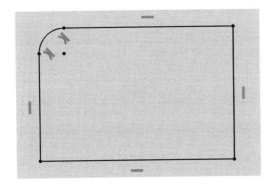

9. Likewise, create fillets at the remaining corners, as shown.

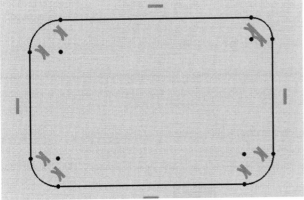

10. Click the **Constrain equal**  icon on the **Sketcher constraints** toolbar.

11. Select the top-right and top-left fillets of the rectangle; the fillets are made equal.

12. Select the top-left and bottom-left fillets of the rectangle.

13. Select the bottom-left and the bottom-right fillets of the rectangle.

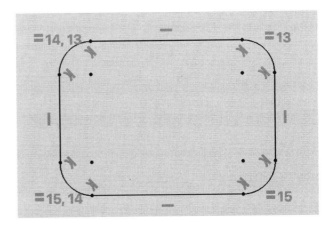

14. Click the **Constrain Coincident**  icon on the **Sketcher constraints** toolbar.

15. Select the center point of the top right fillet of the rectangle.

16. Select the center point of the top right fillet of the external geometry.

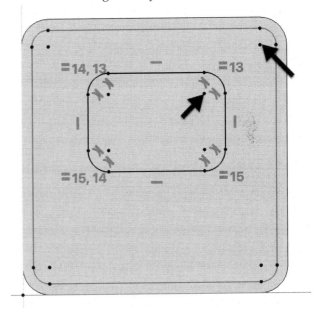

17. Select the center point of the bottom-left fillet of the rectangle.

18. Select the center point of the bottom-left fillet of the external geometry.

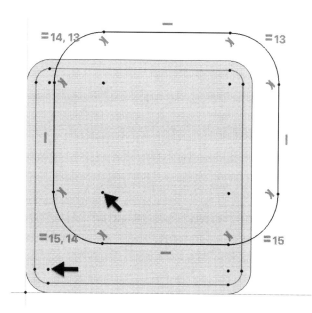

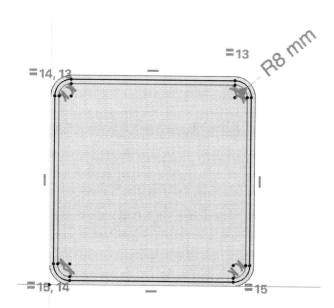

The centerpoints of the fillets are coincident with each other.

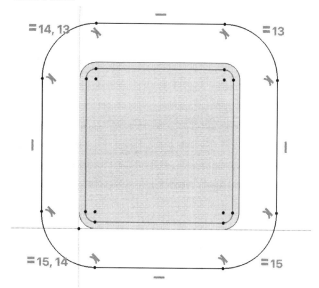

23. Likewise, create another rectangle with fillets.

- Click the **Rectangle** [icon] icon on the **Sketcher geometries** toolbar.
- Create a rectangle, as shown.

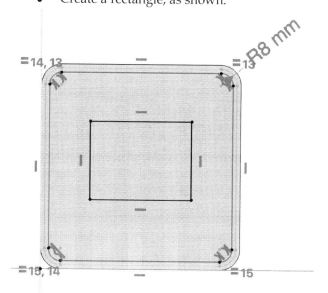

19. Click **Constrain diameter** drop-down > **Constrain radius** on the **Sketcher constraints** toolbar.

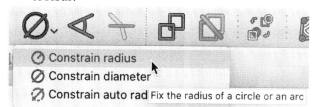

20. Select any one of the fillets of the rectangle.
21. Type 8 in the **Radius** box.
22. Click **OK**.

- Click the **Create fillet** [icon] icon on the **Sketcher geometries** toolbar.
- Create fillets at the corners of the rectangle, as shown.

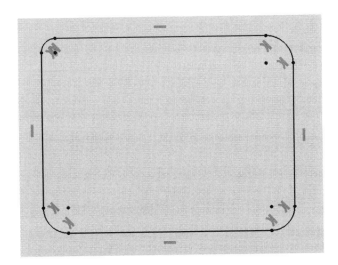

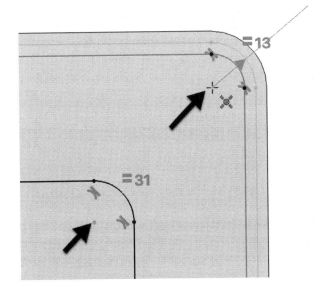

- Click the **Constrain equal** icon on the **Sketcher constraints** toolbar.
- Select the top-right and top-left fillets of the rectangle; the fillets are made equal.
- Select the top-left and bottom-left fillets of the rectangle.
- Select the bottom-left and the bottom-right fillets of the rectangle.

- Select the center point of the bottom-left fillet of the rectangle.
- Select the center point of the bottom-left fillet of the external geometry.

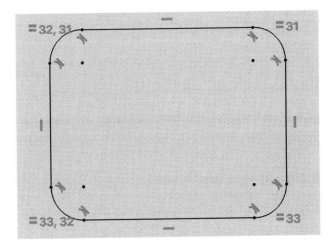

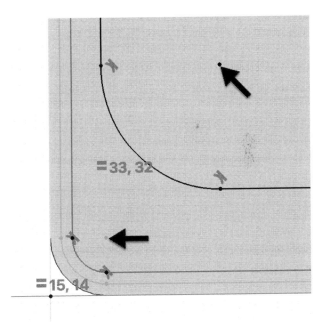

- Click the **Constrain Coincident** icon on the **Sketcher constraints** toolbar.
- Select the center point of the top right fillet of the rectangle.
- Select the center point of the top right fillet of the external geometry.

- The centerpoints of the fillets are coincident with each other.

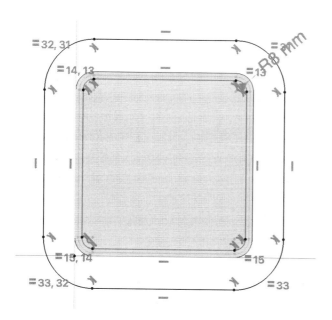

- Click **Constrain Diameter** drop-down > **Constrain radius** 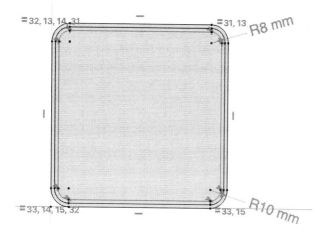 on the **Sketcher constraints** toolbar.
- Select any one of the fillets of the rectangle.
- Type 10 in the **Radius** box.
- Click **OK**.

24. Click **Leave Sketch** on the **Sketcher** toolbar.
25. Click the **Pocket** icon on the **Part Design Modeling** toolbar.
26. Type **10** in the **Length** box in the **Pocket parameters** dialog.
27. Click **OK**.

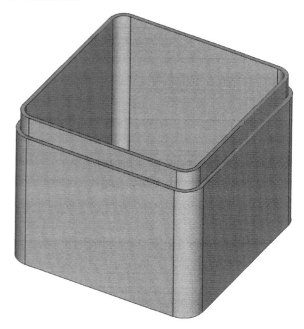

28. Save and close the file.

Chapter 3: Assembly Basics

In this chapter, you will:

- Add Components to assembly
- Apply constraints between components

TUTORIAL 1

This tutorial takes you through the creation of your first assembly.

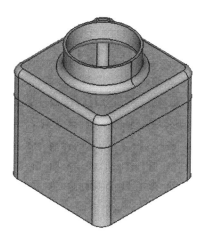

Starting a New Assembly File

1. Open the **FreeCAD** application.
2. Click **Tools > Addon Manager** on the Menu bar.
3. On the **Addon Manager** dialog, select **Workbenches** from the **Show Addons containing** drop-down.
4. Select **A2plus** from the list.
5. Click **Install**.
6. Click **Close**.
7. Close the FreeCAD application, and then restart it.
8. Click **File > New** on the Menu bar.
9. Select **Workbenches** drop-down > **A2plus**.

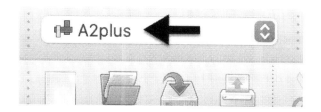

Inserting the Base Component

1. Click **File > Save** on the menu bar.
2. Type **Assembly_tutorial** in the **File name**.
3. Click **Save**.
4. To insert the base component, click the **Add a part from an external file** icon on the **A2p_Part** toolbar.

Add a part from an external file

Add a part from an external file to the assembly
(a2p_ImportPart) (⇧A)

5. Browse to the location of the **Tutorial 2** file of Chapter 1, and then double-click on it.

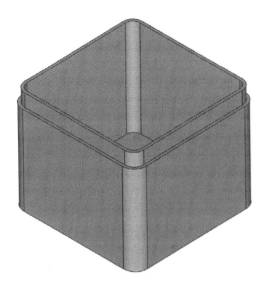

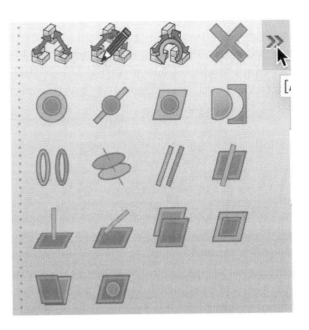

Adding the second component

1. To insert the second component, click **A2plus > Add a part from an external file** on the Menu bar.

2. Browse to the location of the **Tutorial** 1 file of Chapter 1, and then double click on it.

3. Click in the window to place the component.

Different assembly constraints that can be applied are given next.

 **Add circularEdge constraint:** This constraint is used to make two circular edges concentric.

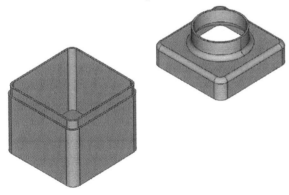

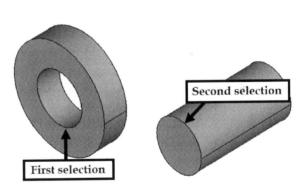

Applying Constraints

After adding the components to the assembly environment, you need to apply constraints between them. By applying constraints, you establish relationships between components.

The **A2p_Constraint** toolbar has various tools to apply constraints between the components.

Click the **Flip direction** 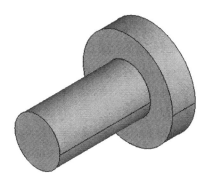button on the **Constraint Properties** dialog to reverse the direction.

Click the **Toggle** button on the **Constraint Properties** dialog to lock/unlock the rotation of the component.

Add planeCoincident Constraint: Using this constraint, you can make two planar faces coplanar to each other.

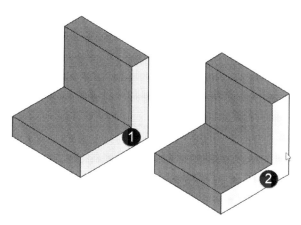

You can change the direction in which the planar faces touch each other. To do this, click the **Flip direction** button on the **Constraint Properties** dialog.

You can also change the direction by using the **Direction** drop-down. To do this, select an option from the **Direction** drop-down located in the **Constraint Properties** dialog.

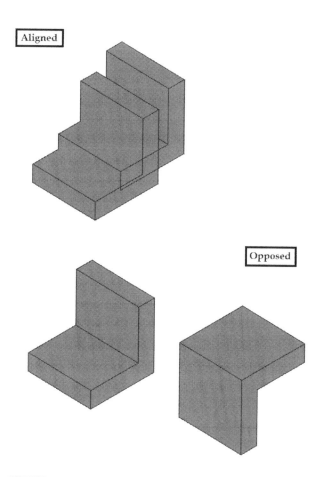

Add axial Coincident Constraint: This constraint allows you to align the centerlines of the round faces. Select the two cylindrical faces to be aligned.

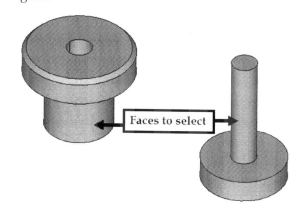

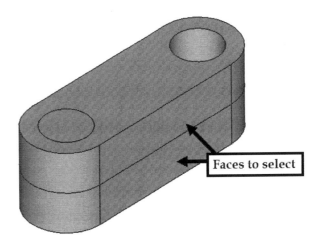

Click the **Flip direction**  button on the **Constraint Properties** dialog; the axes of the selected round faces are positioned in the direction opposite to each other.

On the **Constraint Tools** dialog, click the **Add angledPlanes constraint** icon. On the **Constraints Properties** dialog, type 45 in the **Angle** box. Click the **Accept** button.

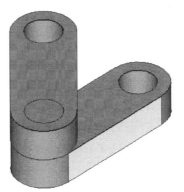

Add angledPlanes constraint: Applies the angle constraint between two components. Activate the **Define Constraints** command select the faces to be constrained.

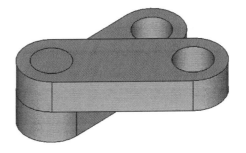

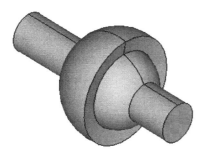 **Add sphereCenterIdent constraint:** This constraint is used to align two spherical surfaces.

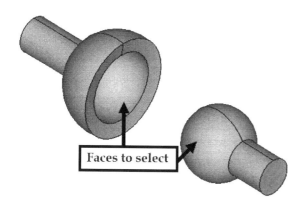

1. Click the **Define Constraints** icon on the **A2p_Constraint** toolbar.

Define constraints

Opens a dialog to define constraints *(a2p_ConstraintDialogCommand)*

2. Press and hold the CTRL key, and then click on the planar faces of the two parts, as shown.

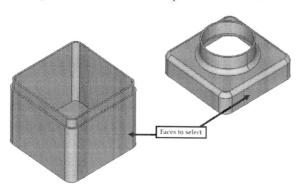

3. On the **Constraint Tools** dialog, click the **Add planeCoincident Constraint** icon.

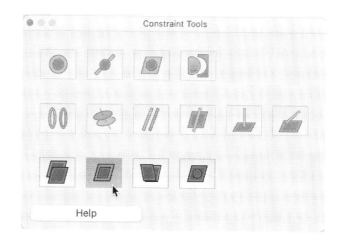

4. On the **Constraint Properties** dialog, select **Direction > aligned**.
5. Click the **Accept** button on the **Constraint Properties** dialog.
6. Press and hold the CTRL key, and then select the planar faces of the two parts, as shown.

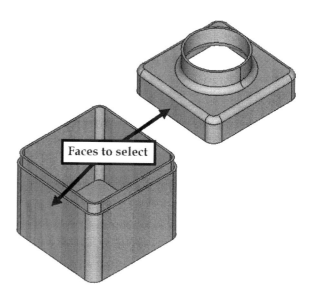

7. On the **Constraint Tools** dialog, click the **Add planeCoincident Constraint** icon.
8. On the **Constraint Properties** dialog, select **Direction > aligned**.
9. Click the **Accept** button on the **Constraint Properties** dialog.

10. Click the **Print detailed DOF information** icon on the **A2p_view** toolbar. The degrees of freedom are displayed.

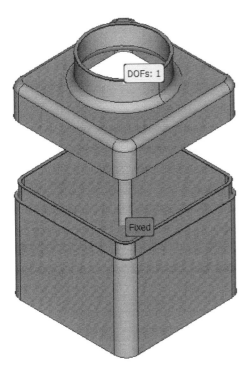

You need to remove this degree of freedom.

11. Click the **Move the selected part under**

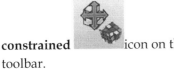

   constrained icon on the **A2p_part** toolbar.

12. Press and hold the pointer on the second part and then drag it upward.

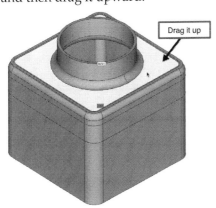

13. Press and hold the CTRL key and select the first face.

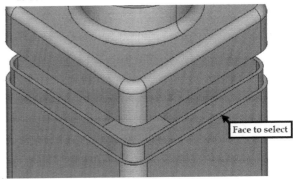

14. Press and hold the CTRL key and select the second face, as shown.

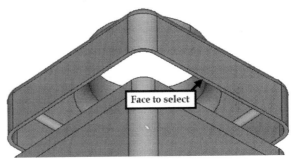

15. On the **Constraint Tools** dialog, click the **Add planeCoincident Constraint** icon.

16. On the **Constraint Properties** dialog, select **Direction > opposed**.

17. Click the **Accept** button on the **Constraint Properties** dialog.

18. Close the **Constraint Tools** dialog.

19. Click the **Print detailed DOF information**  icon on the **A2p_view** toolbar.

The assembly is constrained fully.

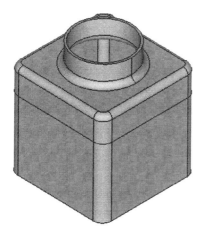

20. Click **File > Save** on the Menu bar.
21. Click **File > Close** on the Menu bar.

Chapter 4: Sketching

In this chapter, you learn the sketching tools. You learn to create:

- Polylines
- Polygons
- Slots
- Constraints
- B-Splines
- Ellipses
- Circles
- Trim
- Extend
- Toggle Construction geometry

Creating Polylines

The **Create Polyline** tool is the most commonly used while creating a sketch.

1. To start a new part file, click **File > New** on the Menu Bar.
2. On the **Workbench** toolbar, select **Workbench** drop-down > **Part Design**.
3. Click **Sketch > Create Sketch** on the Menu bar.
4. Select the **XY_Plane**, and then click **OK**. The sketch starts.
5. To activate this tool, you need to click the **Create Polyline**  icon on the **Sketcher geometries** toolbar.
6. Click in the graphics window and move the pointer.
7. Click to create a line. Notice that another line is attached to the cursor.

8. Move the pointer and click to create another line.

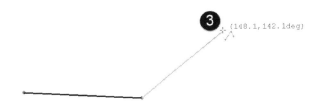

9. Press the **M** key on your keyboard.
10. Move the pointer and click to create a line perpendicular to the previous line.

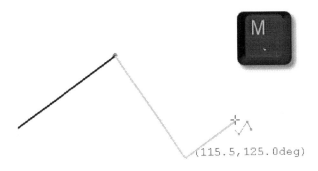

11. Press the **M** key twice on your keyboard.
12. Move the pointer and click to create a line colinear to the previous line.

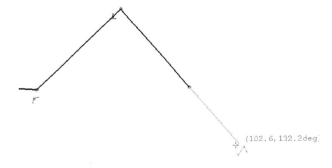

13. Press the **M** key thrice on your keyboard; a grey arc tangent to the previous line appears.

14. Move the pointer and click to create an arc tangent to the previous line.

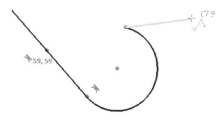

15. Press the **M** key four times to display an arc normal to the previous line.
16. Again, press the **M** key to change the direction of the normal arc.

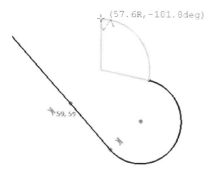

17. Click to create the normal arc.
18. Right click to end the line chain.
19. Again, right click to deactivate the **Create Polyline** tool.

Creating Polygons

A Polygon is a shape having many sides ranging from 3 to 1024. In FreeCAD, you can create regular polygons having sides with equal length. Follow the steps given next to create a polygon.

1. Click the **Create Sketch** icon on the **Sketcher** toolbar.
2. Select the **XY_Plane**, and then click **OK**. The sketch starts.
3. On the **Sketcher geometries** toolbar, select

   Polygon > Regular Polygon.
4. On the **Create array** dialog, type **8** in the **Number of Sides** box.
5. Click **OK**.
6. Click to define the center of the polygon.
7. Move the pointer and click to define the size and angle of the polygon.

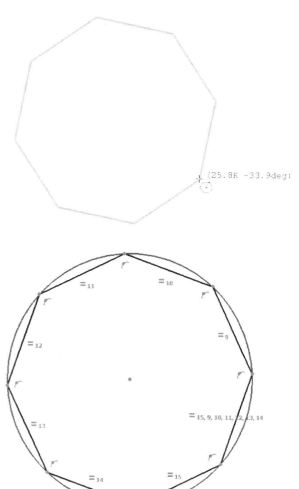

Creating a Slot

The **Create Slot** tool is used to create slots.

1. Click the **Create Slot** 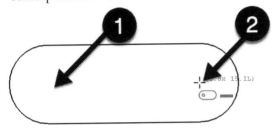 icon on the **Sketcher geometries** toolbar.
2. Click to specify the centerpoint of the first semicircle.
3. Move the pointer and click to specify the centerpoint of the second semicircle.

Constraints

Constraints are used to control the shape of a sketch by establishing relationships between the sketch elements. You can add constraints using the tools available on the **Sketcher constraints** toolbar.

Constrain Coincident

This constraint connects a point to another point.

1. On the **Sketcher constraints** toolbar, click **Constrain Coincident** .
2. Select two points. The selected points are connected.

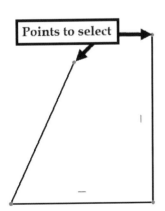

Constrain horizontally

To apply the **Horizontal** constraint, click on a line and click the **Constrain Horizontally** ▬ icon on the **Sketcher constraints** toolbar.

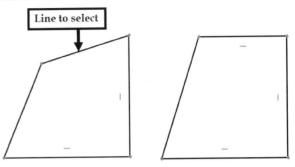

Constrain Vertically

Use the **Constrain Vertically** ▮ icon to make a line vertical.

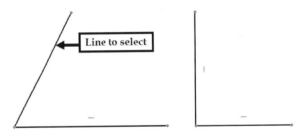

Constrain tangent

This constraint makes an arc, circle, or line tangent to another arc or circle. Click the **Constrain Tangent** icon on the **Sketcher constraints** toolbar. Select a circle, arc, or line. Next, select another circle or arc; the two elements are tangent to each other.

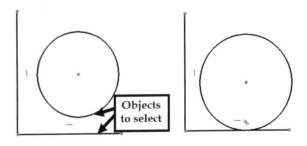

Constrain Parallel

Use the **Constrain Parallel** icon to make two lines parallel to each other. To do this, click the **Constrain Parallel** icon on the **Sketcher constraints**. Next, select the two lines to be parallel.

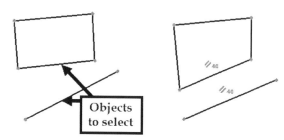

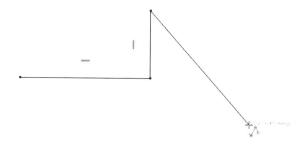

Constrain Perpendicular

Use the **Constrain Perpendicular** ⊥ icon to make two entities perpendicular to each other.

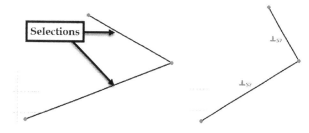

Auto Constraints

FreeCAD automatically adds constraints when you create sketch elements.

1. Start a new sketch and activate the **Create Polyline** tool from the **Sketcher geometries** toolbar.
2. Click to specify the start point of the line.
3. Move the pointer in the horizontal direction.
4. Click to create a line with the **Horizontal** constraint.

5. Move the pointer vertically in the upward direction .
6. Click to create a line with the **Vertical** constraint.

7. Create an inclined line, as shown.

8. Right-click twice to deactivate the tool.

Deleting Constraints

Select the constraint and press **Delete** on your keyboard.

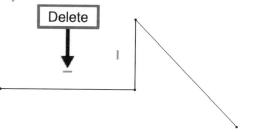

Constrain symmetrical

Use the **Constrain symmetrical** tool to make two sketch elements symmetric about a centerline.

1. Click on the elements to make symmetric.
2. Click on the symmetry line.
3. Click the **Constrain symmetrical** ⊁ icon on the **Sketcher constraints** toolbar.

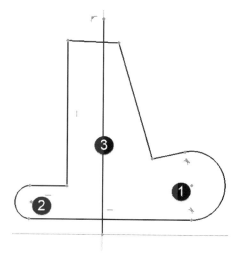

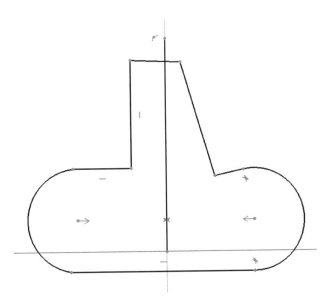

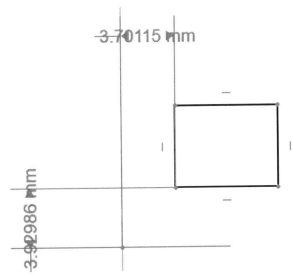

Constrain Lock

The **Constrain Lock** constraint locks a selected point by adding dimensions to it.

1. On the **Sketcher constraint** toolbar, click the

   Constrain Lock 🔒 icon.
2. Select a point from the sketch.

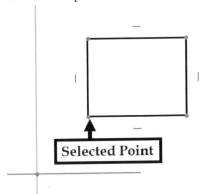

Dimensions are created between the selected point and the origin.

Constrain Block

This constraint fixes the sketch object at its location.

1. Click the **Constrain Block** ⊗ icon on the **Sketcher constraints** toolbar.
2. Select an object from the sketch.

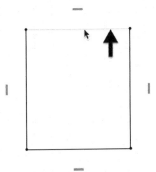

3. Click the object and drag; notice that it is fixed at its location.

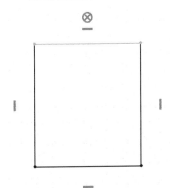

Hiding Constraints

To hide sketch constraints, uncheck the checkbox next to it in the **Constraints** section located in the **Combo View** panel.

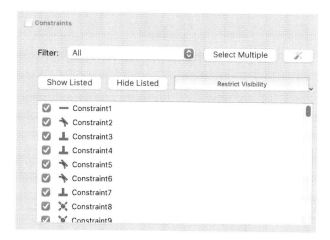

Create B-Spline

This command creates a smooth B-spline curve using the control points you select.

1. On the **Sketcher geometries** toolbar, click **B-Spline** drop-down > **Create B-Spline** .
2. Click to define points in the graphics window.

3. Right click to create a spline controlled by the selected points.
4. Press Esc to deactivate this command.

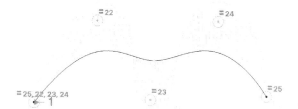

Create periodic B-spline

If you want to create a closed B-spline, then click the **B-spline** drop-down > **Create periodic B-spline** 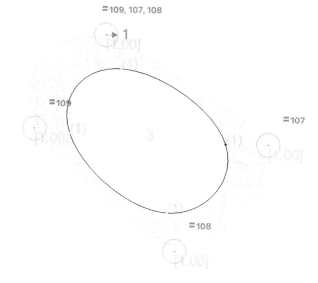 on the **Sketcher geometries** toolbar. Next, specify the control points. Right click to create a closed B-spline.

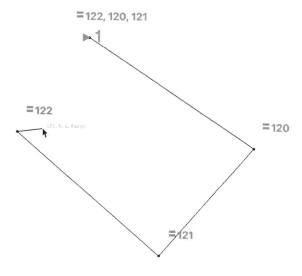

Ellipses

Ellipses are also non-uniform curves, but they have a regular shape. They are splines created in regular closed shapes.

1. Click the **Create Sketch** icon on the **Sketcher** toolbar.

2. Select any one of the datum planes from the **Combo View** panel.
3. Click **OK**.
4. On the **Sketcher geometries** toolbar, click **Conic** 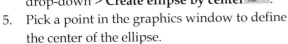 drop-down > **Create ellipse by center** .
5. Pick a point in the graphics window to define the center of the ellipse.
6. Move the pointer and click to define the radius and orientation of the first axis.

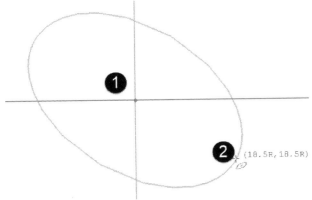

7. Move the pointer and click to define the radius of the second axis.

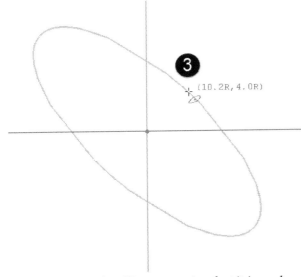

Click and drag the ellipse to notice that it is under-defined. You need to add dimensions and constraints to fully define the ellipse.

8. On the **Sketcher constraints** toolbar, click

Constrain angle .
9. Select the lines, as shown.

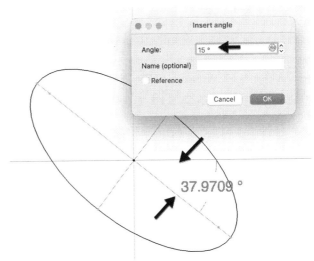

10. Type 15 in the **Angle** box and click **OK**.
11. Click the **Constrain distance** icon on the **Sketcher constraints** toolbar.
12. Select the major axis line.
13. Type 25 in the **Length** box and click the **OK** button.

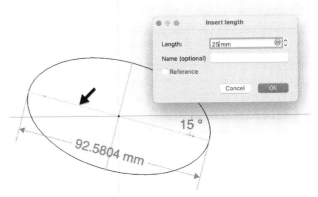

14. Likewise, add the distance constrain to the minor axis. The sketch is fully defined.

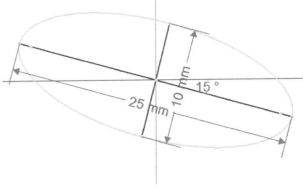

Extend Edge

The **Extend Edge** tool is used to extend lines, arcs, and other open entities to connect to other objects.

1. Create a sketch, as shown below.

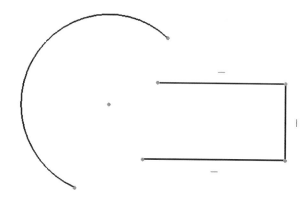

2. Click the **Extend edge** icon on the **Sketcher geometries** toolbar.
3. Select the horizontal open line.
4. Select the arc; the line is extended up to the arc.

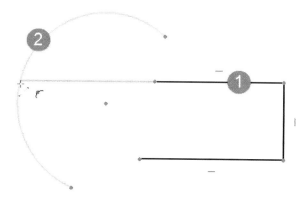

Likewise, extend the other elements, as shown.

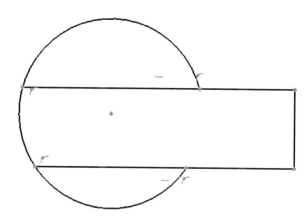

Trim Edge

The **Trim Edge** tool is used to trim the unwanted portions of the sketch using an intersecting edge.

1. Click the **Trim Edge** icon on the **Sketcher geometries** toolbar.
2. Click on the edges to trim.

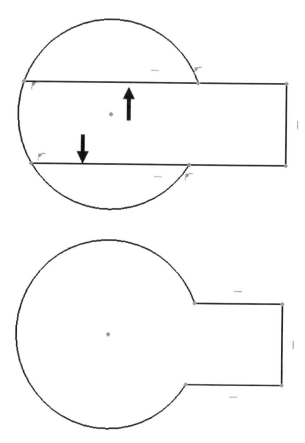

Constrain point onto object

This constraint makes a point coincident with a sketch element.

1. Click the **Constrain point onto object** icon on the **Sketcher constraints** toolbar.
2. Select the point and object, as shown.

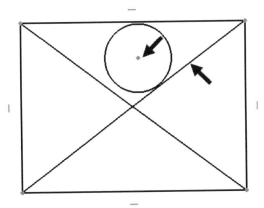

construction element, click on it and select **Toggle Construction geometry** on the **Sketcher geometries** toolbar.

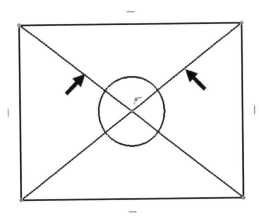

The point is made coincident with the object. Likewise, make the point coincident with another object, as shown.

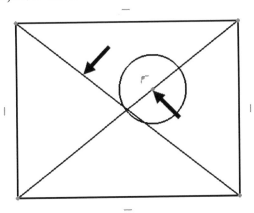

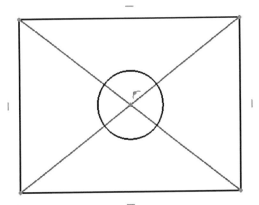

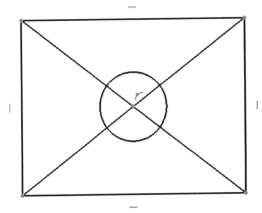

You can also convert it back to a standard sketch element by clicking on it and selecting the **Toggle Construction geometry** icon on the **Sketcher geometries** toolbar.

TUTORIAL 1

In this tutorial, you create the sketch shown in the figure.

Toggle Construction geometry

This command converts a standard sketch element into a construction element. Construction elements support you to create a sketch of a desired shape and size. To convert a standard sketch element to

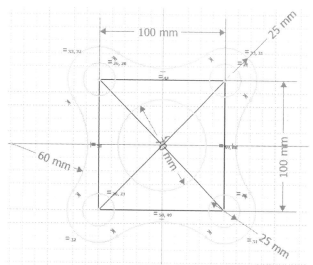

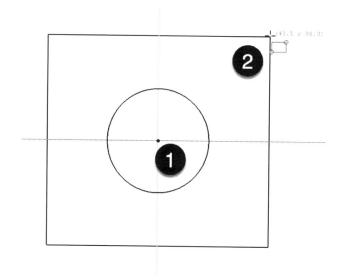

1. Open the FreeCAD application.
2. Click **File > New** on the Menu bar.
3. Select the **Part Design** option from the **Workbenches** drop-down.
4. Click the **Create sketch** icon on the **Part Design Helper** toolbar, and then select the XY Plane.
5. Click **OK** to start the sketch.
6. Click the **Create Circle** icon on the **Sketcher geometries** toolbar.
7. Select the origin point of the sketch.
8. Move the pointer outward and click to create a circle.
9. On the **Sketcher geometries** toolbar, click the **Rectangle** drop-down > **Centered Rectangle** (or) click **Sketch > Sketcher geometries > Create centered rectangle**.

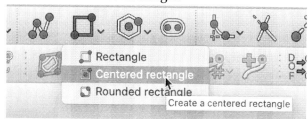

10. Select the origin point of the sketch.
11. Drag the cursor towards the top right corner, and then click to create a rectangle.

12. Click the **Create Circle** icon on the **Sketcher geometries** toolbar.
13. Select the top-left corner point of the rectangle.
14. Move the pointer outward and click to create a circle.

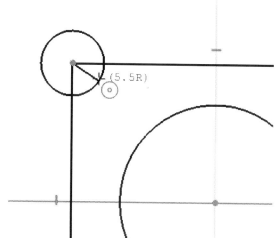

15. Likewise, create three more circles on the remaining corners.

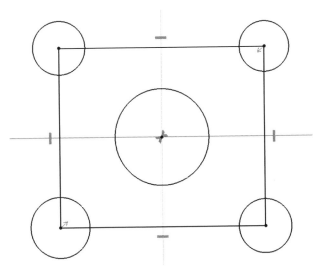

16. Select the edges of the rectangle.

17. Click **Toggle Construction geometry** 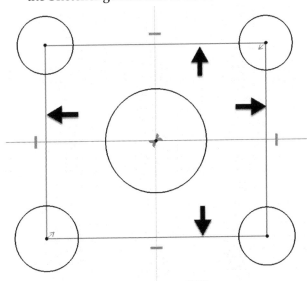 on the **Sketcher geometries** toolbar.

18. Click the **Constrain equal** icon on the **Sketcher constraints** toolbar.

19. Select the circles located on the corner points of the rectangle (start from the top-left corner circle).

20. Select the bottom-left and top-left circles; the diameters of the circles are made equal.

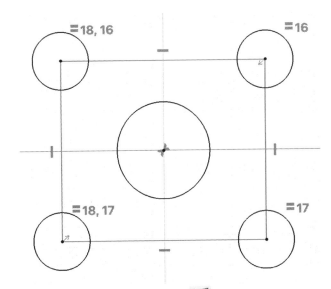

21. Click **Constrain distance** on the **Sketcher constraints** toolbar.

22. Select the vertical line of the rectangle.

23. Type 100 in the **Length** box, and then click **OK**.

24. Select the horizontal line of the rectangle.

25. Type 100 in the **Length** box, and then click **OK**.

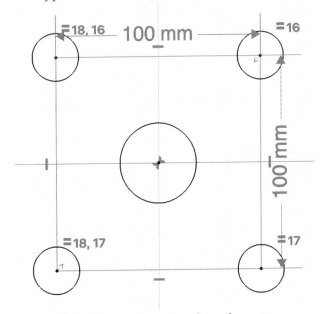

26. Click the **Constrain radius** drop-down > **Constrain diameter** on the **Sketcher constraints** toolbar.

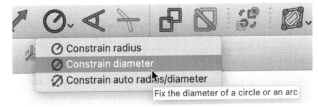

27. Select the circle located at the center.
28. Type **70** in the **Diameter** box and click **OK**.

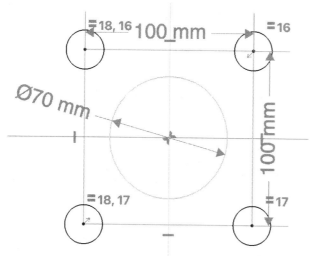

29. Select any one of the circles located on the corner points of the rectangle.
30. Type **25** in the **Diameter** box, and click **OK**.

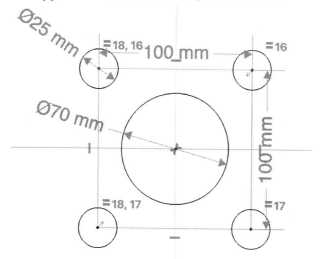

31. Click the **Create Circle** ◉ icon on the **Sketcher geometries** toolbar.
32. Create circles on the corner points of the rectangle, as shown.

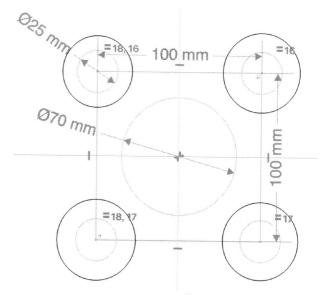

33. Click the **Constrain equal** ⯐ icon on the **Sketcher constraints** toolbar.
34. Select the newly created circles.
35. Select the bottom-left and top-left circles; the diameters of the circles are made equal.

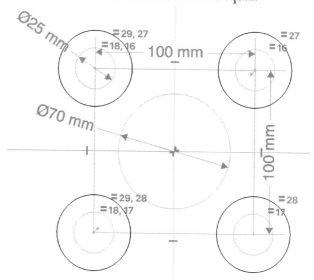

36. Click **Arc** drop-down > **End points and rim point** on the **Sketcher geometries** toolbar.

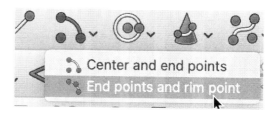

37. Select the outer circle located on the top-left

corner.

38. Select the outer circle located on the bottom-left corner.

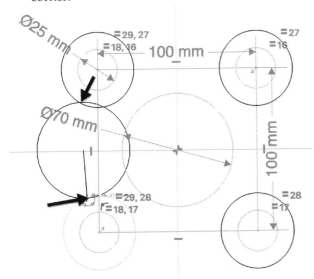

39. Move the pointer toward the right and click to create an arc.

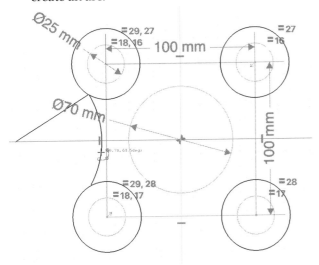

40. Likewise, create three more arcs, as shown.

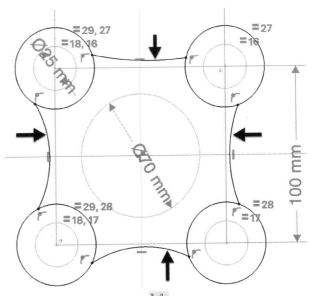

41. Click the **Trim Edge** icon on the **Sketcher geometries** toolbar.

42. Click on the edges to trim, as shown.

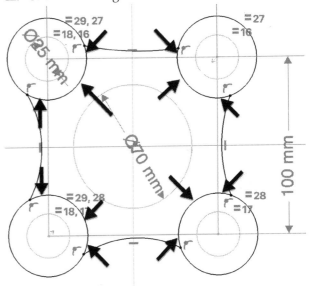

43. Click the **Constrain tangent** icon on the **Sketcher constraints** toolbar.

44. Create the tangent constraints between the entities, as shown.

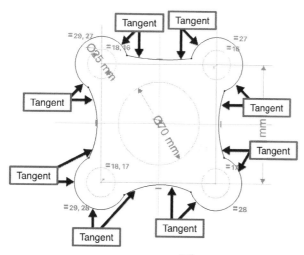

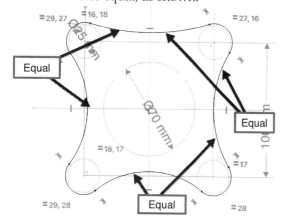

45. Click the **Constrain equal** icon on the **Sketcher constraints** toolbar.
46. Make the arcs equal, as shown.

47. Click the **Constrain diameter** drop-down. > **Constrain radius** icon on the **Sketcher constraints** toolbar.
48. Select any one of the arcs concentric to the circles.
49. Type **25** in the **Radius** box and click **OK**.
50. Select any one of the tangent arcs.
51. Type **60** in the **Radius** box and click **OK**.

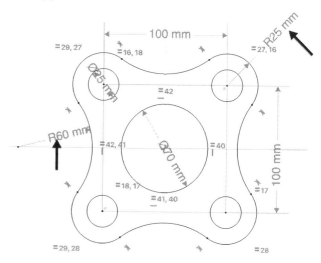

52. Click **Leave Sketch** on the **Sketcher** toolbar.
53. Save and close the file.

Chapter 5: Additional Modeling Tools

In this chapter, you create models using additional modeling tools. You learn to:

- Create slots
- Create circular patterns
- Create holes
- Create chamfers
- Create shells
- Create coils
- Create a loft feature
- Create a sweep feature

TUTORIAL 1

In this tutorial, you create the model shown in the figure:

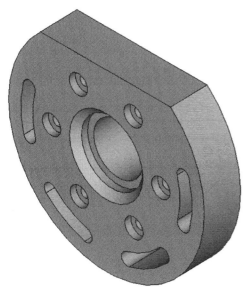

Creating the First Feature

1. Open the FreeCAD application.
2. Click **File > New** on the Menu bar.
3. Select the **Part Design** option from the **Workbenches** drop-down.
4. Click **Edit > Preferences** on the Menu bar.

The **Preferences** dialog box appears. If you are working on MacOS, then click **FreeCAD > Preferences** on the title bar.

5. Click the **Units** tab on the **Preferences** dialog.
6. Select **User system > Imperial decimal**.
7. Type **3** in the **Number of decimals** box.
8. Click **OK**.

9. Click the **Create sketch** icon on the **Part Design Helper** toolbar, and then select the XZ Plane.
10. Click **OK** to start the sketch.
11. Deactivate the **Toggle Construction geometry** icon on the **Sketcher geometries** toolbar.
12. Click the **Create Circle** icon on the **Sketcher geometries** toolbar.
13. Select the origin point of the sketch.
14. Move the pointer outward and click to create a circle.

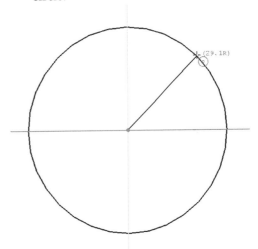

15. Click the **Create Line** icon on the **Sketcher geometries** toolbar.
16. Specify a point at the location outside the circle, as shown.

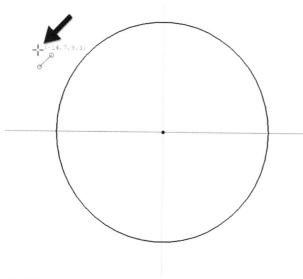

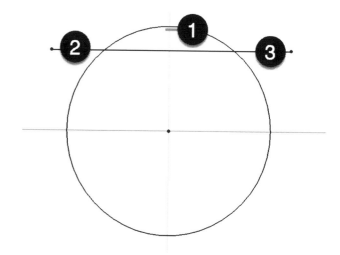

17. Move the pointer horizontally and notice the Horizontal constraint symbol.
18. Click outside the circle — Press Esc to deactivate the **Create Line** tool.

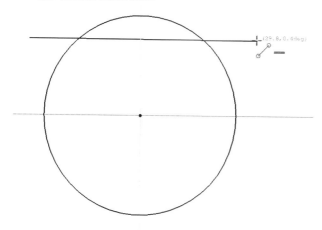

19. Click the **Trim Edge** 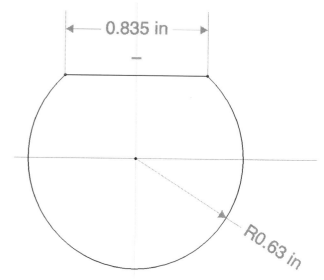 icon on the **Sketcher geometries** toolbar.
20. Click on the portions of the sketch to be trimmed, as shown below.

21. Add the **Radius** and **Horizontal Distance** constraints to the sketch.

22. Click the **Close** button on the **Combo View** panel.
23. Click the **Pad** icon on the **Part Design Modeling** toolbar.
24. Type **0.236** in the **Length** box and click **OK**.

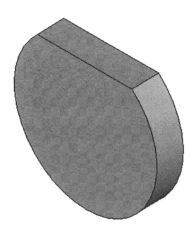

Creating the Pocket feature

1. Click on the front face of the model.

2. Click the **Create Sketch** icon on the **Part Design Helper** toolbar.

3. On the **Sketcher geometries** toolbar, click **Arc drop-down > Center and end points** .

4. Select the origin as the center point.

5. Move the cursor outside and click in the first quadrant of the circle to specify the start point of the arc.

6. Move the cursor and click in the fourth quadrant of the circle to specify the endpoint of the arc.

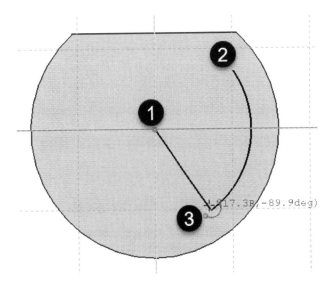

7. Likewise, create another centerpoint arc, as shown.

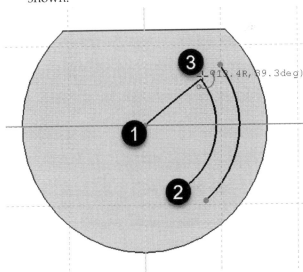

8. On the **Sketcher geometries** toolbar, click **Arc drop-down > End points and rim point** .

9. Zoom to the first quadrant.

10. Select the endpoint of the first and second arcs, as shown.

11. Move the pointer outward and click to specify the rim point of the arc.

50

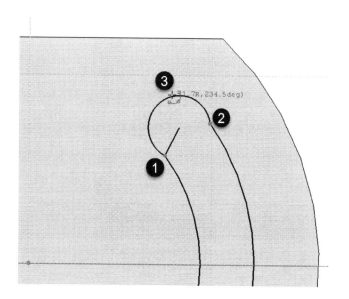

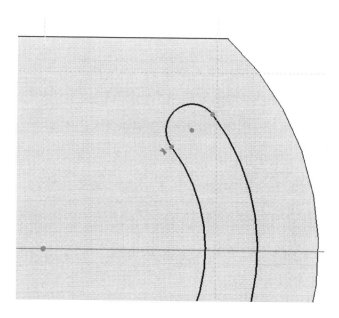

12. Use the **Constrain Coincident** tool and connect the endpoints of the small arc to the endpoints of the centerpoint arcs, if they are not correctly connected.

13. Click the **Constrain Tangent** icon on the **Sketcher constraints** toolbar.

14. Select the small arc and anyone of the centerpoint arcs; the small arc is made tangent to the centerpoint arc.

15. Click **OK** on the **Sketcher Constraint Substitution** message box.

16. Likewise, make the small arc tangent to the other center point arc.

17. Likewise, create a small arc on the other ends of the centerpoint arcs.

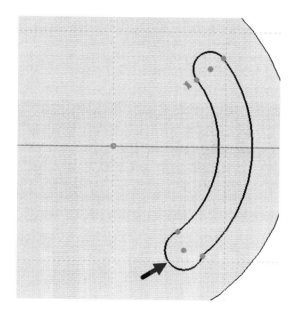

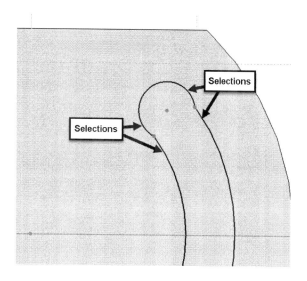

18. Use the **Constrain Coincident** tool and connect the endpoints of the small arc to the endpoints of the centerpoint arcs, if they are not correctly connected.

19. Make the small arc tangent to the centerpoint arcs.

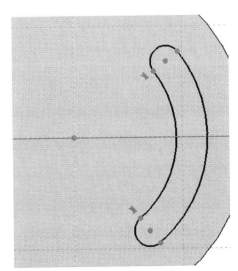

20. Activate the **Toggle Construction geometry** icon on the **Sketcher geometries** toolbar.

21. Click the **Create Line** icon on the **Sketcher geometries** toolbar.

22. Select the origin point of the sketch.

23. Select the centerpoint of the small arc.

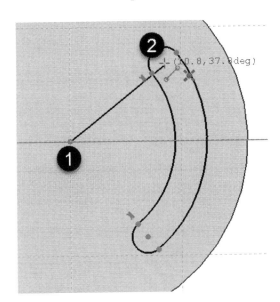

24. Likewise, create a line by selecting the origin and center point of another small arc.

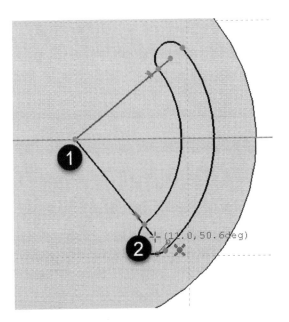

25. Use the **Constrain Coincident** tool and connect the endpoint of the line and the center point of the small arc, if not correctly connected.

26. Click the **Toggle construction geometry** icon on the **Sketcher geometries** toolbar.

27. Click the **Constrain distance** icon on the **Sketcher constraints** toolbar.

28. Select any one of the lines.

29. Type 0.512 in the **Length** box and click **OK**.

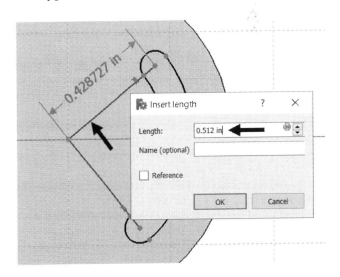

30. Click the **Constrain diameter** drop-down > **Constrain Radius** icon on the **Sketcher constraints** toolbar.

31. Select any one of the small arcs.

32. Type 0.039 in the **Radius** box, and then click **OK**.

33. Click the **Constrain angle** ◁ icon on the **Sketcher constraints** toolbar.

34. Select the two lines.

35. Type **30** in the **Angle** box, and then click **OK**.

36. Select the horizontal axis of the sketch and anyone of the lines.

37. Type **15** in the **Angle** box, and then click **OK**.

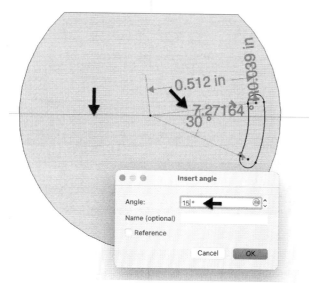

38. Click **Close** on the **Combo View** panel.

39. Click the **Pocket** 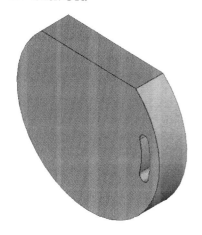 icon on the **Part Design Modeling** toolbar.

40. Select **Type > Through All** from the **Pocket Parameters** dialog.

41. Click **OK**.

Creating a Polar Pattern

1. Click the **Polar Pattern** icon on the **Part Design Modeling** toolbar.
2. Select the **Pocket** feature from the **Select Feature** section in the **Combo View** panel.
3. Click **OK**.
4. Select **Axis > Normal sketch axis**.
5. Type **180** in the **Angle** box.
6. Type **4** in the **Occurrences** box.
7. Check the **Reverse direction** option.
8. Click **OK**.

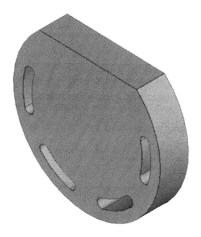

Adding the Pad feature

1. Press and hold the middle and right mouse button.
2. Drag the pointer to rotate the model.
3. Click on the back face of the model.

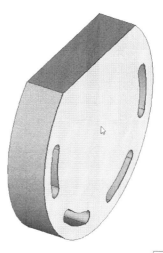

4. Click the **Create Sketch** icon on the **Part Design Helper** toolbar.

5. Click the **Create Circle** icon on the **Sketcher**

geometries toolbar.

6. Select the sketch origin.

7. Move the pointer outward and click to create the circle.

8. Click the **Constrain diameter drop-down > Constrain auto radius/diameter** on the **Sketcher constraints** toolbar.

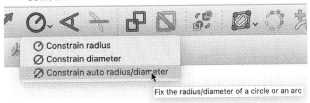

9. Select the circle.

10. Type **0.472** in the **Diameter** box and click **OK**.

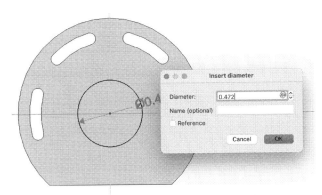

11. Click **Close** on the **Combo View** panel.

12. Click the **Pad** icon on the **Part Design Modeling** toolbar.

13. Type **0.078** in the **Length** box.

14. Click **OK**.

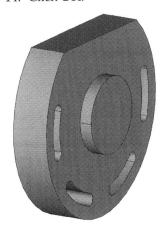

Creating a Counterbore Hole

In this section, you create a counterbore hole concentric to the circular face.

1. Select the front face of the model.

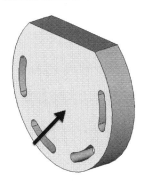

2. Click the **Create Sketch** icon on the **Part Design Helper** toolbar.

3. Click **OK** on the **Combo View** panel.

4. Click the **Create Circle** icon on the **Sketcher geometries** toolbar.

5. Select the origin point of the sketch.

6. Move the pointer outward and click to create a circle.

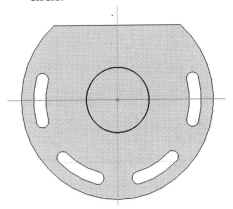

7. Click **Close** on the **Combo View** panel.

8. Click the **Hole** icon on the **Part Design Modeling** toolbar.

9. Type **0.314** in the **Diameter** box.

10. Select **Depth > Through All**.

11. On the **Hole Parameters** section, under **Hole cut**, select **Type > Counterbore**.

12. Type **0.394** in the **Diameter** box.

13. Type **0.078** in the **Depth** box.

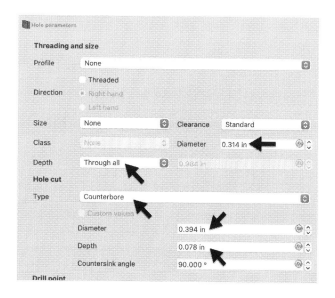

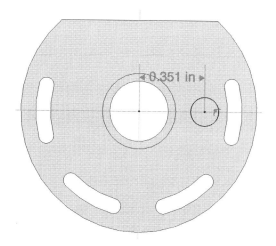

14. Click **OK** on the **Combo View** panel; the counterbore hole is created.

Creating Threaded holes

In this section, you create a threaded hole.

1. Click on the front face of the model.

2. Click the **Create Sketch** icon.

3. Click the **Create Circle** icon on the **Sketcher geometries** toolbar.

4. Click on the horizontal axis on the right side.

5. Move the pointer outward and click to create the circle.

6. Add the horizontal distance constraint between the centerpoint of the circle and the origin point.

7. Click the **Close** button on the **Combo View** panel.

8. Click the **Hole** icon on the **Part Design Modeling** toolbar; the **Hole Parameters** section appears.

9. Under **Threading and size**, select **Profile > UTS coarse profile**.

10. Check the **Threaded** option.

11. Select **Direction > Right hand**.

12. Select **Size > #1**.

13. Select **Class > 2B**.

14. Select **Depth > Through all**.

15. Under **Hole cut**, select the **Counterbore** option from the **Type** drop-down.

16. Set the Counterbore **Diameter** to 0.118.

17. Set the Counterbore **Depth** to 0.039.

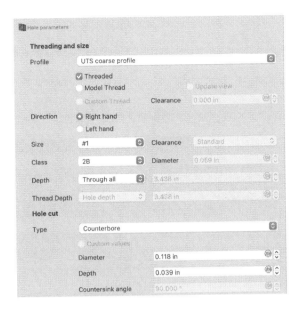

18. Click **OK** to create the hole.

19. Click the **Polar Pattern** 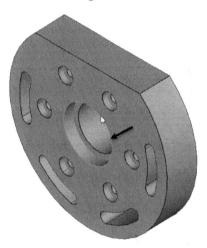 icon on the **Part Design Modeling** toolbar.
20. Select the newly created **Hole** feature from the **Select Feature** section in the **Combo View** panel.
21. Click **OK**.
22. Select **Axis > Normal sketch axis**.
23. Type **360** in the **Angle** box.
24. Type **6** in the **Occurrences** box.
25. Click **OK**.

Creating Chamfers

1. Select the circular edge of the counterbore hole.

2. Click the **Chamfer** icon on the **Part Design Modeling** toolbar.
3. Enter 0.039 in the **Size** box.

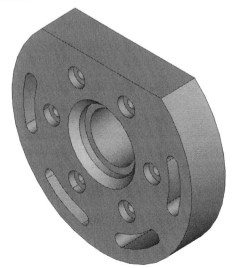

4. Click **OK** to create the chamfer.
5. Save the model and close it.

TUTORIAL 2

In this tutorial, you create the model shown in the figure.

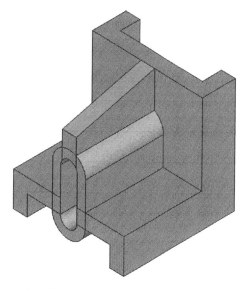

Creating the first feature

1. Open a new FreeCAD file.
2. Select the **Part Design** from the **Workbenches** drop-down.
3. Click the **Create sketch** 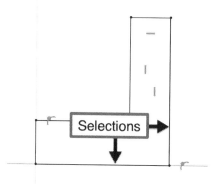 icon on the **Part Design Helper** toolbar, and then select the YZ Plane.
4. Click **OK** to start the sketch.
5. Draw the sketch using the **Polyline** tool, as shown.

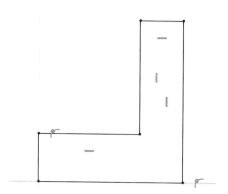

6. Click the **Constrain Equal** icon on the **Sketcher constraints** toolbar.

7. Select the vertical and horizontal lines, as shown.

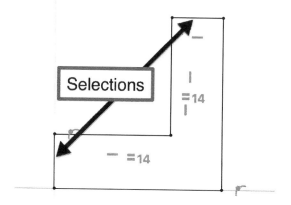

8. Select the two lines to make them equal in length.

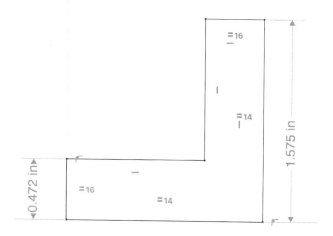

9. Click the **Constraint Vertical** icon on the **Sketcher constraints** toolbar.
10. Add the constraints to the vertical lines, as shown.

11. Click **Leave Sketch** on the **Part Design Helper** toolbar.

12. Click the **Pad** icon on the **Part Design Modeling** toolbar.
13. Select the **Symmetric plane** option from the **Pad parameters** section.
14. Set the **Length** to 1.575.
15. Click **OK** to create the first feature.

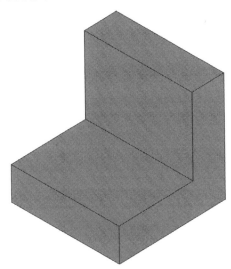

Creating the Shell feature

You can create a shell feature by removing the face of the model and applying thickness to other faces.

1. Press and hold the Ctrl key.
2. Select the top face and the back face of the model.

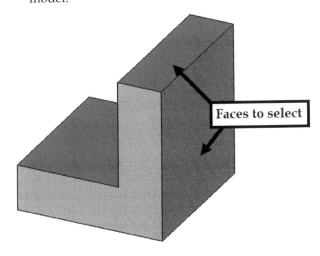

Faces to select

3. Click the **Thickness** icon on the **Part Design Modeling** toolbar.
4. Set **Thickness** to 0.197.
5. Select **Join type > Intersection**.

6. Check the **Make thickness inward** option.

Now, you need to select more faces.

7. Click the **Add face** button.
8. Select the front face.
9. Click the **Add face** button and the bottom face of the model.

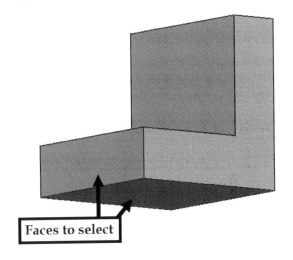

Faces to select

10. Click **OK** to shell the model.

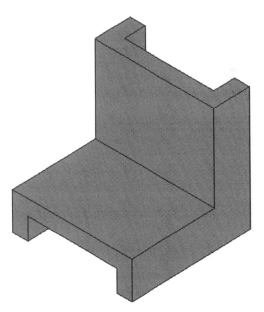

Creating the Third feature

1. Select the front face of the model.

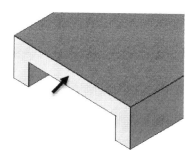

2. Click the **Create Sketch** 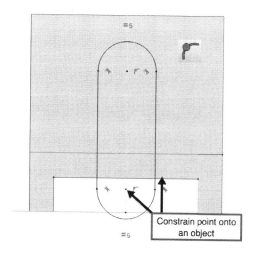 icon on the **Part Design Helper** toolbar.

3. Click the **External geometry** icon on the **Sketcher geometries** toolbar.

4. Select the edges of the model, as shown.

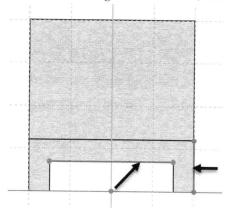

5. Click **Create Slot** on the **Sketcher geometries** toolbar.

6. Draw a slot by selecting the first and second points, as shown.

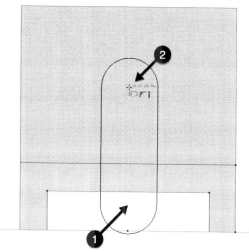

7. Add constraints to the slot.

Constrain point onto an object

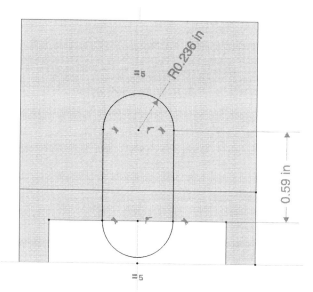

8. Click **Leave Sketch** on the **Part Design Helper** toolbar.

9. Click the **Pad** icon on the **Part Design Modeling** toolbar.

10. Select the **Up to face** option from the **Type** drop-down.

11. Select the back face of the model.

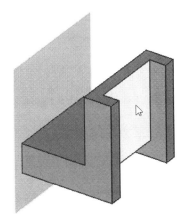

12. Click **OK** to create the feature.

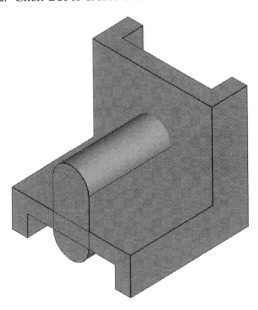

Creating the Rib Feature

In this section, you create a rib feature in the middle of the model. To do this, you must create an offset plane.

1. Select the right face of the model.
2. To create an offset plane, click the **Create a datum plane** ◇ icon on the **Part Design Helper** toolbar.

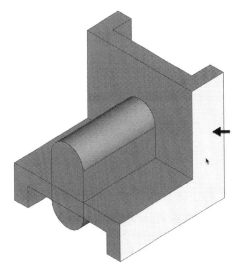

3. Type **0.7875** in the **Z** box available in the **Attachment** section.
4. Check the **Flip sides** option.

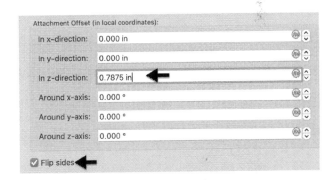

5. Click **OK** to create the plane.

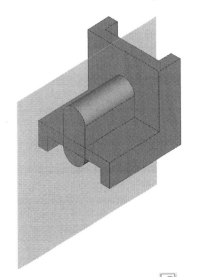

6. Click the **Create Sketch** ⬚ icon on the **Part Design Helper** toolbar.

7. Select the newly created plane.
8. Click **OK**.
9. On the **View** toolbar, set the **Draw Style** to Wireframe .
10. Click the **External Geometry** icon on the **Sketcher geometries** toolbar.
11. Select the model edges, as shown.

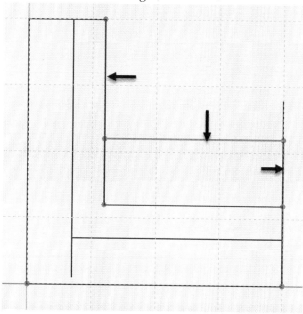

12. Draw the sketch, as shown below.

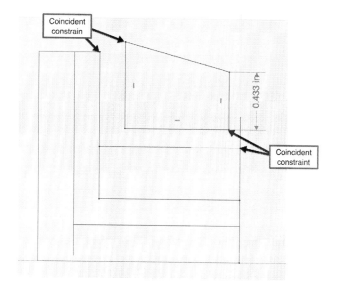

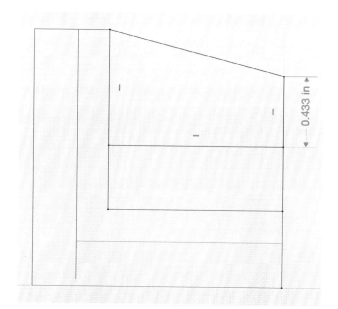

13. Click **Close** on the **Combo View** panel.
14. On the **View** toolbar, set the **Draw Style** to **Flat Lines** .
15. Click the **Pad** icon on the **Part Design Modeling** toolbar.
16. Check the **Symmetric to plane** option.
17. Type **0.197** in the **Length** box.
18. Click **OK** to create the rib feature.

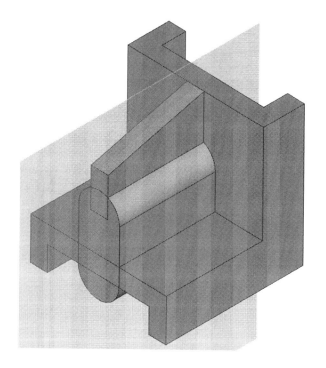

Creating a Pocket Feature

1. Select the front face.

2. Click the **Create Sketch** icon on the **Part Design Helper** toolbar.

3. Click **OK**.

4. Create the sketch, as shown below.

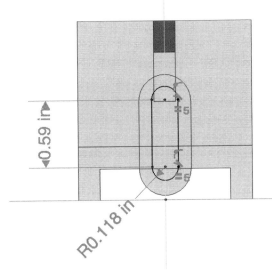

5. Click **Close** on the **Combo View** panel.

6. Click the **Pocket** icon on the **Part Design Modeling** toolbar.

7. Select the **Through All** option from the **Type** drop-down.

8. Click **OK** to create the pocket feature.

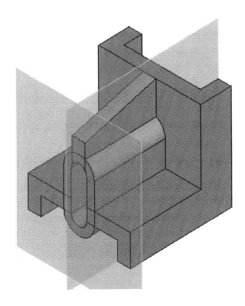

19. Save the model and close it.

TUTORIAL 3

In this tutorial, you create a helical spring.

Creating the Profile

1. Open a new FreeCAD file.

2. Select **Part Design** from the **Workbenches** drop-down.

3. Click the **Create Sketch** icon on the **Part Design Helper** toolbar.

4. Select the XZ Plane from the **Combo View** panel.

5. Click **OK**.

6. Create a circle, as shown.

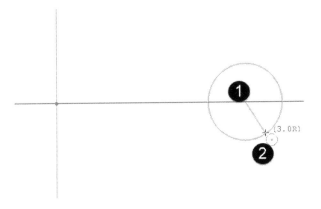

7. Add constraints to it, as shown.

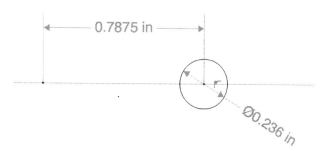

8. Click **Close** on the **Combo View** panel.

Creating the Helix

1. Select **Part** from the **Workbenches** drop-down.

2. Click the **Create primitives** icon on the **Solids** toolbar.

3. In the **Geometric Primitives** dialog, select **Helix** from the drop-down.

4. Type **0.59** in the **Pitch** box.

5. Type **4.72** in the **Height** box.

6. Type **0.7875** in the **Radius** box.

7. Select **Right-handed** from the **Coordinate system** drop-down.

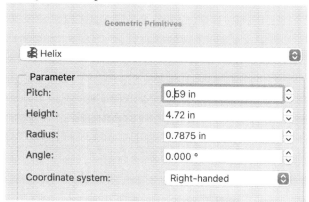

8. Expand the **Location** section.

9. Type **0** in the **X**, **Y**, and **Z** boxes.

10. Click the **Create** button.

11. On the **View** toolbar, click the **Isometric** icon.

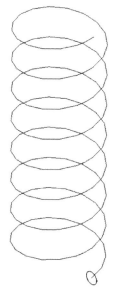

12. Click the **Close** button.

Creating the Sweep

1. Click the **Sweep** icon on the **Part tools** toolbar.

2. Select the **Sketch** from the **Available profiles** section.

3. Click the **Add** button.

4. Check the **Create solid** option.

5. Click the **Sweep Path** button.

6. Select the helix.

7. Click **Done**.

8. Click **OK** to create the sweep.

9. Save the model and close the file.

TUTORIAL 4

In this tutorial, you create a shampoo bottle using the **Loft**, **Pad**, and **Sweep** tools.

Creating the Loft feature

To create a loft feature, you need to create sections.

1. Start a new FreeCAD file.
2. Select the **Part Design** option from the **Workbenches** drop-down.
3. Click the **Create Sketches** icon on the **Part Design Helper** toolbar.
4. Select the XY Plane and click **OK**.
5. Click the **Ellipse** drop-down > **Create ellipse by center** on the **Sketcher geometries** toolbar.

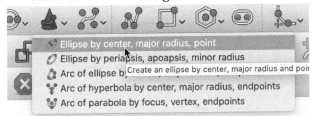

6. Draw the ellipse by selecting the points, as shown.

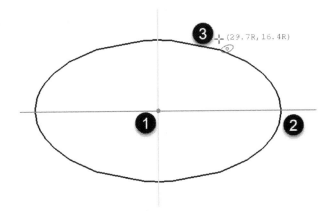

7. On the **Sketcher constraints** toolbar, click the **Constrain distance** icon.
8. Select the horizontal axis of the ellipse.
9. Type **3.50** in the **Length** box of the **Insert Length** dialog.
10. Click **OK**.
11. Select the vertical axis of the ellipse.
12. Type **1.968** in the **Length** box of the **Insert Length** dialog.
13. Click **OK**.

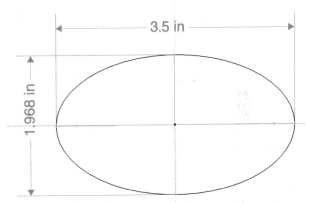

14. Click the **Close** button on the **Combo View** panel.
15. Click the **Create a datum plane** icon on the **Part Design Helper** toolbar.
16. Click on the ellipse.
17. Type 1.5 in the **Z** box.
18. Click **OK**.

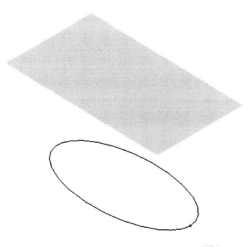

19. Click the **Create a datum plane**  icon on the **Part Design Helper** toolbar.
20. Click on the newly created plane.
21. Type 1.5 in the **Z** box.
22. Click **OK.**

27. Click the **Create a datum plane** icon on the **Part Design Helper** toolbar.
28. Click on the newly created plane.
29. Type 1.2 in the **Z** box.
30. Click **OK.**

23. Click the **Create a datum plane** icon on the **Part Design Helper** toolbar.
24. Click on the newly created plane.
25. Type 1.2 in the **Z** box.
26. Click **OK.**

31. Click the **Create a datum plane**  icon on the **Part Design Helper** toolbar.
32. Click on the newly created plane.
33. Type 1.5 in the **Z** box.
34. Click **OK**.

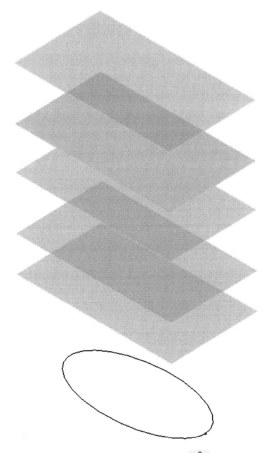

35. Click the **Create a datum plane** icon on the **Part Design Helper** toolbar.
36. Click on the newly created plane.
37. Type 1.2 in the **Z** box.
38. Click **OK**

39. Click the **Create Sketch** icon on the **Part Design Modeling** toolbar.
40. Select the first datum plane, and then click **OK**.

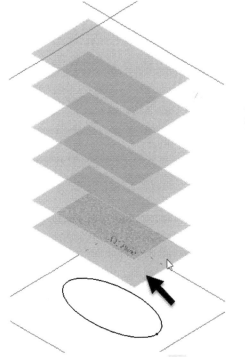

41. Click the **View Section** icon on the **Sketcher** toolbar.
42. Create an ellipse, as shown.

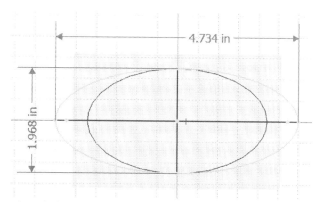

43. Click the **Close** button on the **Combo View** panel.

44. Click the **Create Sketch** 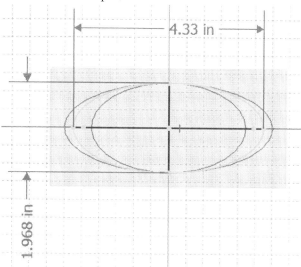 icon on the **Part Design Helper** toolbar.

45. Select the second datum plane, and then click **OK**.

46. On the Menu bar, click **Sketch > View section** 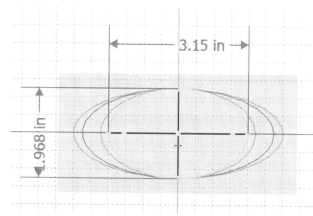.

47. Create an ellipse, as shown.

48. Click the **Close** button on the **Combo View** panel.

49. Start a sketch on the third datum plane.

50. Click the **View Section** icon on the **Sketcher** toolbar.

51. Create an ellipse, as shown.

52. Click the **Close** button on the **Combo View** panel.

53. Start a sketch on the fourth datum plane, and then create an ellipse on it.

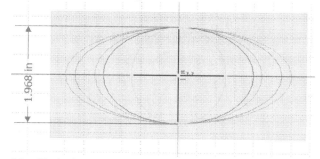

54. Click the **Close** button on the **Combo View** panel.

55. Start a new sketch on the fifth plane.

56. Create an ellipse, as shown.

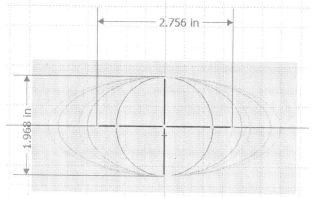

57. Click the **Close** button on the **Combo View** panel.

58. Start a new sketch on the sixth plane.

59. Create a circle, as shown.

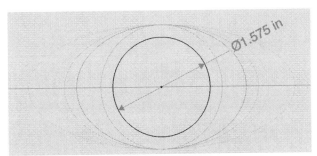

60. Click the **Close** button on the **Combo View** panel.
61. Click in the graphics window to deselect the last sketch.
62. Click the **Additive Loft** icon on the **Part Design Modeling** toolbar.
63. Select the ellipse located at the bottom.
64. Click **OK**.
65. Click the **Add section** button and select the next ellipse.

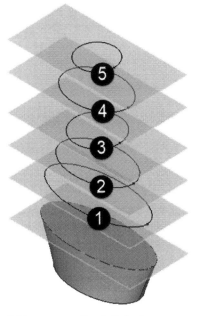

67. Click **OK** to create the loft feature.

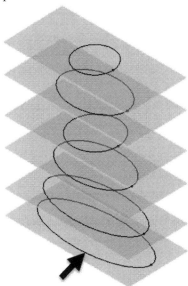

66. Likewise, select the remaining sketches in the order, as shown.

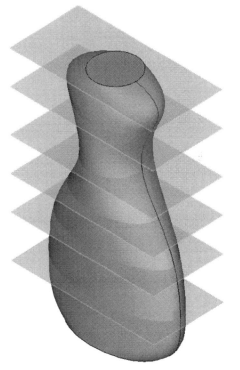

Creating the Extruded feature

1. Click the **Pad** icon on the **Part Design Modeling** toolbar.
2. Check the **Allow used features** option from the **Select Features** dialog.
3. Select the last sketch from the sketch list.

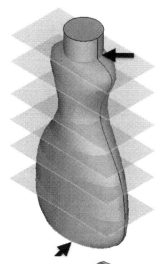

4. Click **OK**.
5. Type **1** in the **Length** box and click **OK**.

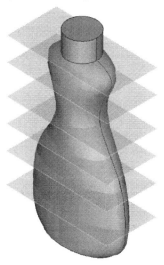

3. Click the **Fillet** icon on the **Part Design Modeling** toolbar.
4. Set **Radius** to 0.2.

Creating Fillets

1. Press and hold the Ctrl key.
2. Click on the bottom and top edges of the swept feature.

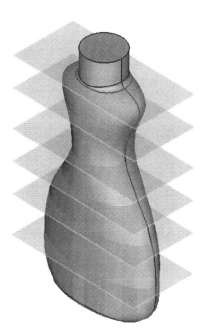

5. Click **OK**.

Shelling the Model

1. Select the top face of the cylindrical feature.

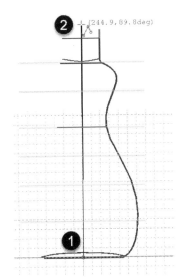

2. Click the **Thickness** 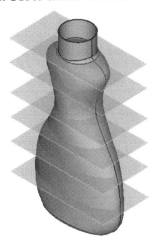 icon on the **Part Design Modeling** toolbar.
3. Set **Thickness** to 0.03.
4. Click **OK** to create the shell.

7. Right click to end the chain.
8. Create a horizontal construction line, as shown.

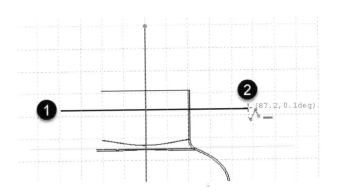

Adding Threads

1. Click the **Create Sketch** icon on the **Part Design Helper** toolbar.
2. Select the XZ Plane, and then click **OK**.
3. Click **Draw Style > Wireframe** on the **View** toolbar.

4. Click the **Toggle Construction geometry** icon on the **Sketcher geometries** toolbar.

5. Click the **Create Polyline** icon on the **Sketcher geometries** toolbar.
6. Select the origin point of the sketch, move the cursor vertically upward and click to create a vertical construction line.

9. Click the **Toggle construction geometry** icon on the **Sketcher geometries** toolbar.
10. Create a closed profile, as shown.

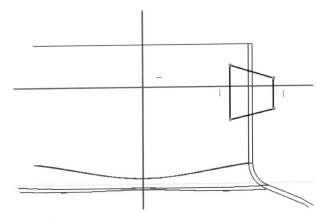

11. Press Esc to deactivate the **Create Polyline** tool.
12. Add fillets, constraints, and dimensions to the

profile.

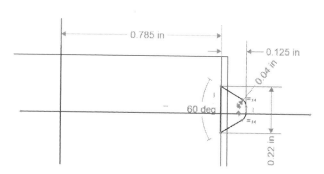

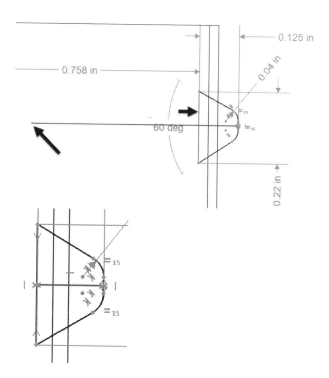

13. Click the **Constrain symmetrical** icon on the **Sketcher constraints** toolbar.
14. Select the right vertical line of the profile.
15. Select the right endpoint of the construction line.

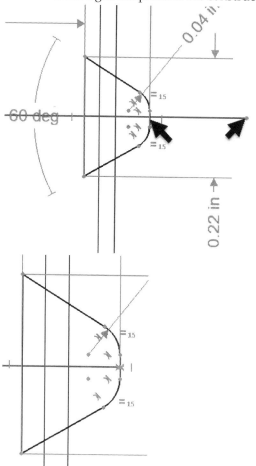

17. Create a **Vertical distance** constraint, as shown.

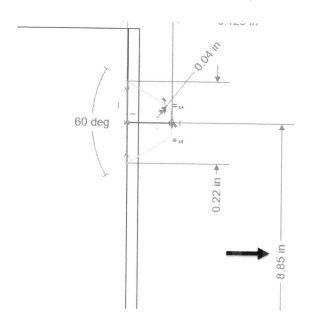

16. Select the left vertical line and the left endpoint of the horizontal construction line.

18. Click the **Close** button on the **Combo View** panel.
19. Select **Draw Style > Flat Lines** from the View toolbar.
20. Click the **Additive Helix** icon on the **Part Design Modeling** toolbar.
21. In the **Helix parameters** dialog, select **Vertical**

sketch axis from the **Axis** drop-down.
22. Select **Mode > Pitch-Height-Angle**.
23. Type **0.27** in the **Pitch** box.
24. Type **0.55** in the **Height** box.
25. Check the **Reveresed** option.

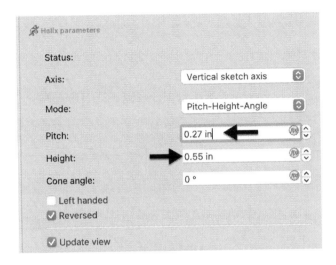

26. Click **OK** to create the additive helix.

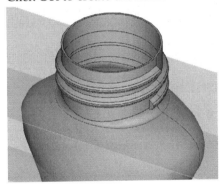

27. Save the model.

TUTORIAL 5

In this tutorial, you create the model, as shown.

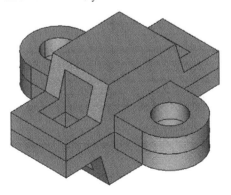

Creating the First feature

1. Open a new FreeCAD file.
2. Select **Part Design** from the **Workbenches** drop-down.
3. Click the **Create Sketch** icon on the **Part Design Helper** toolbar.
4. Select the YZ Plane and click **OK**.
5. On the menu bar, click **Sketch > Sketcher geometries > Create centered Rectangle**.
6. Select the origin point of the sketch.
7. Move the pointer outward and click to create a centered rectangle.
8. Add dimensions to the sketch, as shown.

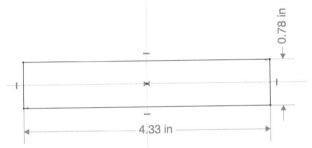

9. Click the **Close** button on the **Combo View** panel.
10. Click the **Pad** icon on the **Part Design Modeling** toolbar.
11. Type **1.575** in the **Length** box.
12. Check the **Symmetric to plane** option.
13. Click **OK**.

14. Click the **Create Sketch** icon on the **Part Design Helper** toolbar.
15. Select the YZ Plane and click **OK**.

16. On the menu bar, click **Sketch > Sketcher geometries > Create Hexagon**.
17. On the menu bar, click **Sketch > View Section**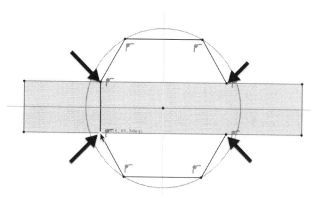
18. Select the sketch origin.
19. Click on the horizontal axis of the sketch.

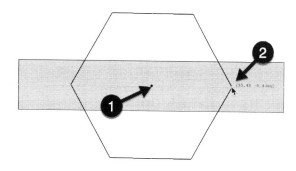

20. On the menu bar, click **Sketch > Sketcher geometries > External geometry**.
21. Select the horizontal edges of the solid body.
22. On the menu bar, click **Sketch > Sketcher geometries > Trim edge**.
23. Select the edges of the hexagon, as shown.

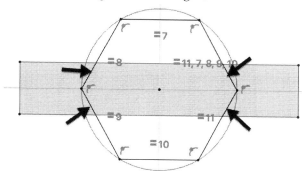

24. On the menu bar, click **Sketch > Sketcher geometries > Create line**.
25. Select the endpoints of the two trimmed lines, as shown.
26. Likewise, select the endpoints of the other two trimmed lines.

27. Add the **Equal** constraint between the lines, as shown.

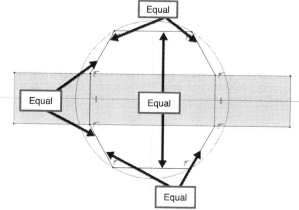

28. Add dimensions and the Horizontal constraint to the sketch, as shown.

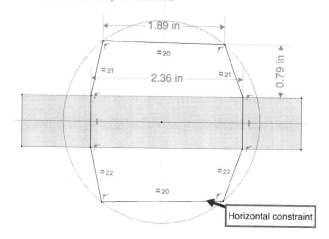

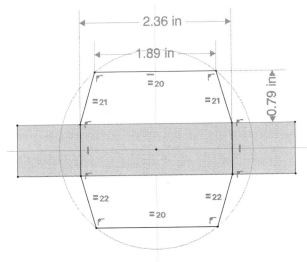

29. Click the **Close** button on the **Combo View** panel.
30. Click the **Pad** icon on the **Part Design Modeling** toolbar.
31. Type **1.575** in the **Length** box.
32. Check the **Symmetric to plane** option.
33. Click **OK**.

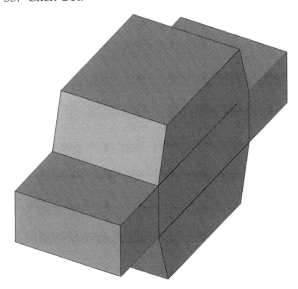

Creating the Second feature

1. Click the **Create Sketch** icon on the **Part Design Helper** toolbar.
2. Select the XY Plane and click **OK**.
3. Select **Draw Style > Wireframe** from the **View** toolbar.
4. Click the **Create Slot** icon on the **Sketcher geometries** toolbar.
5. Click on the horizontal axis on the left side.

6. Move the pointer toward right and click on the horizontal axis.
7. On the menu bar, click **Sketch > Sketcher geometries > Create circle**.
8. Select the centerpoint of the left arc of the slot.
9. Move the pointer outward and click.
10. Likewise, create a circle concentric to the right arc of the slot.
11. Add dimensions to the sketch, as shown.

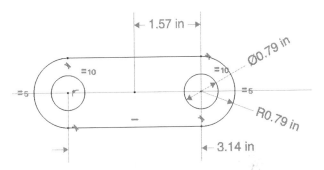

12. Click **Close** on the **Combo View** panel.
13. Click the **Pad** icon on the **Part Design Modeling** toolbar.
14. Type **0.78** in the **Length** box.
15. Check the **Symmetric to plane** option.
16. Click **OK**.
17. Select **Draw Style > Flat Lines** from the **View** toolbar.

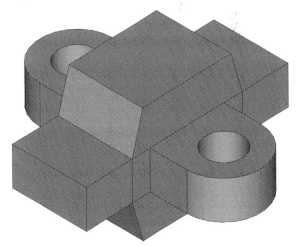

Creating the Pocket Feature

1. Click the **Create Sketch** icon on the **Part Design Helper** toolbar.
2. Select the XY Plane and click **OK**.
3. Change the **Draw Style** to **Wireframe**.
4. Create a rectangle and add constraints to it, as shown.

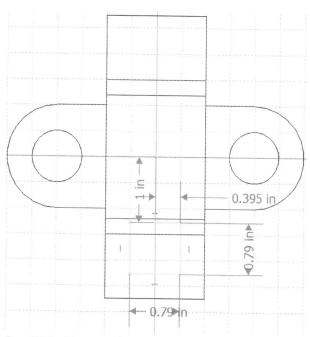

5. Click **Close** on the **Combo View** panel.

6. Click the **Pocket** icon on the **Part Design Modeling** toolbar.

7. Select **Type > Through All**.

8. Check the **Symmetric to plane** option.

9. Click **OK**.

10. Select **Draw Style > Flat Lines** from the **View** toolbar.

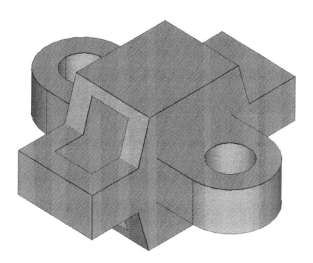

11. Click the **Mirrored** icon on the **Part Design Modeling** toolbar.

12. Select the **Pocket** feature from the **Select feature** list, and then click **OK**.

13. Select the **Base XZ plane** from the **Plane** drop-

down.

14. Click **OK** to mirror the pocket feature.

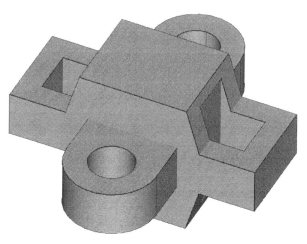

15. Save and close the file.

TUTORIAL 6

In this tutorial, you construct a patterned cylindrical shell.

Constructing a cylindrical shell

1. Start a new FreeCAD file.

2. Select **Part Design** from the **Workbenches** drop-down.

3. Create a sketch on the XY plane (add Diameter constraints to the circles).

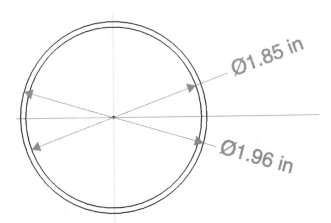

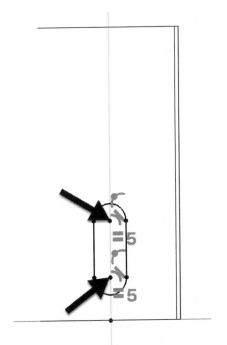

4. Extrude the sketch up to 3.93 depth.

7. Add constraints to the slot.

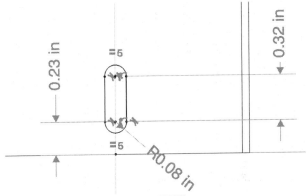

Adding a Slot

1. Activate the **Create Sketch** tool.
2. Select the **XZ Plane** and click **OK**.
3. Set the **Draw Style** to **Wireframe**.
4. Click the **Create Slot** icon on the **Sketcher geometries** toolbar.
5. Click on the vertical axis of the sketch to define the first point of the slot.
6. Move the pointer up and click on the vertical axis to define the second point.

8. Click the **Leave Sketch** icon on the **Part Design Helper** toolbar.
9. Set the **Draw Style** to **Flat Lines** .
10. Click the **Pocket** icon on the **Part Design Modeling** toolbar.
11. On the **Pocket Parameters** section, select **Type > Through All**.
12. Check the **Reversed** option.
13. Click **OK**.

Constructing the Linear and Circular patterns using the MultiTransform tool

1. Click the **MultiTransform** icon on the **Part Design Modeling** toolbar.
2. Select the **Pocket** feature from the **Select feature** list, and then click **OK**.
3. Right-click in the **Transformations** section and select **Add linear pattern**.
4. Select **Direction > Base Z axis**.
5. Type **3.145** in the **Length** box.
6. Type **6** in the **Occurrences** box.
7. Right-click in the **Transformations** section and select **Add polar pattern**.
8. Select the **Base Z axis** from the **Axis** drop-down.
9. Type **360** in the **Angle** box.
10. Type-in **12** in the **Occurrences** box.
11. Click **OK** to create the circular pattern.

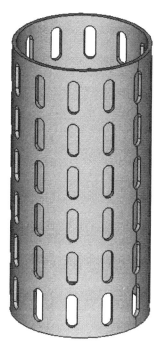

11. Save and close the model.

TUTORIAL 7

In this tutorial, you construct a pulley wheel using the **Revolution** and **Groove** tools.

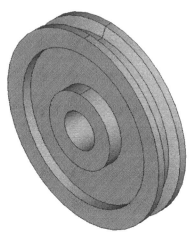

1. Open a new FreeCAD file.
2. Select **Part Design** from the **Workbenches** drop-down.
3. Click the **Create Sketch** icon on the **Part Design Helper** toolbar.
4. Select the YZ plane and click **OK**.
5. Click the **Create Polyline** icon on the **Sketcher geometries** toolbar.
6. Create a closed sketch, as shown.

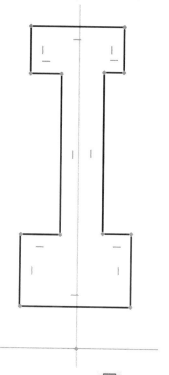

7. Click the **Constrain Equal** icon on the

Sketcher constraints toolbar.

8. Make the entities of the sketch equal in length, as shown.

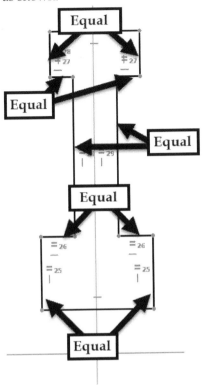

9. Create remaining constraints, as shown.

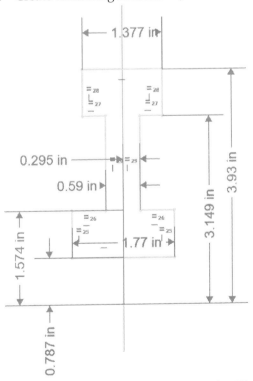

10. Click the **Close** button on the **Combo View**

panel.

11. Click the **Revolution**  icon on the **Part Design Modeling** toolbar; the sketch is selected automatically.
12. Select **Axis > Base Yaxis** from the **Revolution parameters** section of the **Combo View** panel.
13. Type **360** in the **Angle** box.
14. Click **OK** to construct the revolved feature.

Constructing the Groove feature

1. Click the **Create Sketch** icon on the **Part Design Helper** toolbar.
2. Select the YZ Plane and click **OK**.
3. Set the **Draw Style** to **Wireframe**.
4. Create the sketch, as shown.

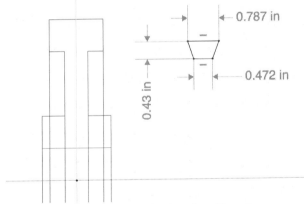

5. On the menu bar, click **Sketch > Sketcher geometries > External geometry**.
6. Select the top horizontal edge of the model, as shown.

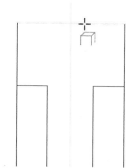

7. On the menu bar, click **Sketch > Sketcher constraints > Constrain point onto object**.
8. Select the endpoint of the sketch and the external geometry, as shown.

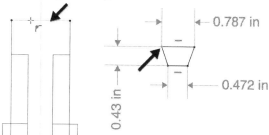

9. On the menu bar, click **Sketch > Sketcher geometries > Create line**.
10. Select the sketch origin, move the pointer vertically upward and click on the external geometry.

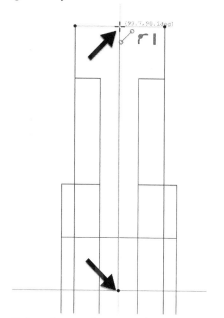

11. Select the newly created vertical line.
12. Click the **Toggle Construction geometry** icon on the **Sketcher geometries** toolbar.
13. Add the Angle constraint between the left inclined line and the bottom horizontal line, as shown.

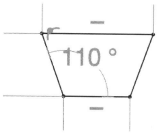

14. Click the **Constraint Symmetrical** icon on the **Sketcher constraints** toolbar.
15. Select the endpoints of the top horizontal line of the sketch.
16. Select the top endpoint of the vertical line.

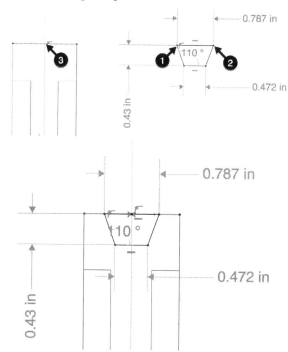

17. Click the **Close** button on the **Combo View** panel.
18. Set the **Draw Style** to **Flat Lines**.
19. Click the **Groove** icon on the **Part Design geometries** toolbar.
20. Select **Axis > Base Yaxis** from the **Revolution parameters** section of the **Combo View** panel.
21. Type 360 in the **Angle** box.
22. Click **OK**.

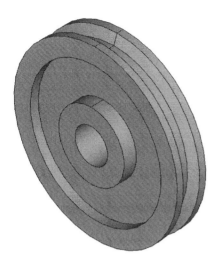

23. Save and close the model.

TUTORIAL 8

In this tutorial, you construct the model shown in the figure.

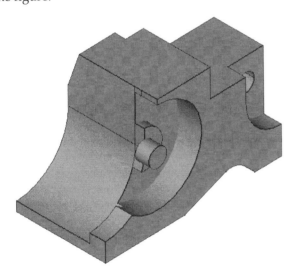

Creating the Base Feature

1. Open a new FreeCAD file.
2. Select **Part Design** from the **Workbenches** drop-down.
3. Click the **Create Sketch** icon on the **Part Design Helper** toolbar.
4. Select the YZ plane and click **OK**.
5. Click the **Create Rectangle** icon on the **Sketcher geometries** toolbar.
6. Specify the first and second corners of the rectangle, as shown.

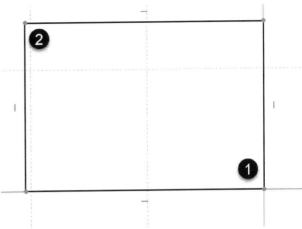

7. Create another rectangle by specifying its first and second corners, as shown.

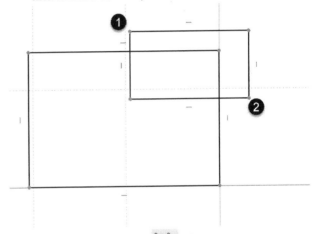

8. Click the **Trim Edge** icon on the **Sketcher geometries** toolbar.
9. Select the elements of the rectangles to be trimmed, as shown.

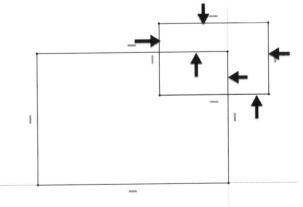

10. Add vertical and horizontal distance constraints to the sketch, as shown.

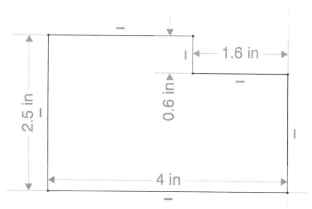

11. Click **Close** on the **Tasks** tab of the **Combo View** panel.
12. Click the **Pad** icon on the **Part Design Modeling** toolbar; the sketch is selected automatically.
13. Type 2 in the **Length** box.
14. Check the **Symmetric to Plane** option.
15. Click **OK**.

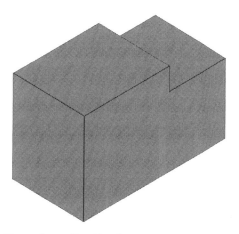

Creating the Pocket Features
1. Click the **Create Sketch** icon on the **Part Design Helper** toolbar.
2. Select the YZ plane and click **OK**.
3. On the menu bar, click **Sketch > View Section**.
4. Click the **Create Polyline** 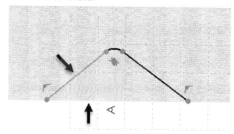 icon on the **Sketcher geometries** toolbar.
5. Specify the endpoints of the polyline, as shown.

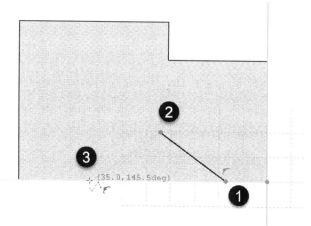

6. Right-click.
7. Click the **Create Fillet** icon on the **Sketcher geometries** toolbar.
8. Select the corner point of the sketch, as shown.

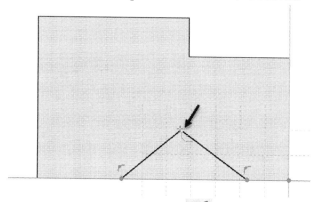

9. Click the **Constrain Angle** icon on the **Sketcher constraints** toolbar.
10. Select the inclined line and the horizontal axis of the sketch.

11. Type **20** in the **Angle** box and click **OK**.
12. Select the other inclined line and the horizontal axis of the sketch, as shown.

81

Additional Modeling Tools

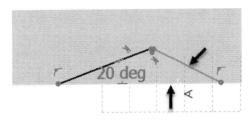

13. Type **135** in the **Angle** box and click **OK**.

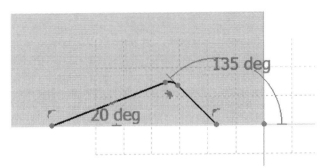

14. Add vertical and horizontal distance constraints to the sketch, as shown.
15. Add the radius constraint to the fillet.

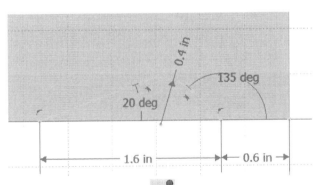

16. Click the **Create line** icon on the **Sketcher geometries** toolbar.
17. Select the endpoints of the sketch, as shown.

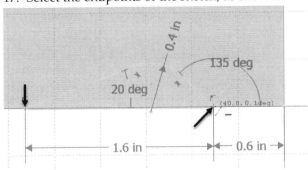

18. Click **Close** on the **Tasks** tab of the **Combo View** panel.
19. Click the **Pocket** icon on the **Part Design**

Modeling toolbar; the sketch is selected automatically.

20. On the **Pocket parameters** dialog, select **Type > Through all**.
21. Check the **Symmetric to plane**.
22. Click **OK** to create the pocket feature.

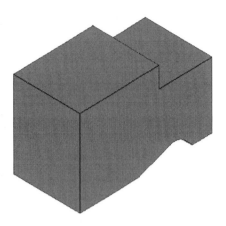

23. Click on the right side face of the model.

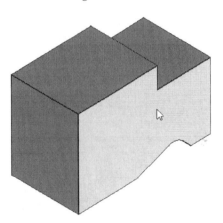

24. Click the **Create Sketch** icon on the **Part Design Helper** toolbar.
25. Click the **Create Polyline** icon on the **Sketcher geometries** toolbar.
26. Click on the vertical axis of the sketch to define the start point.

82

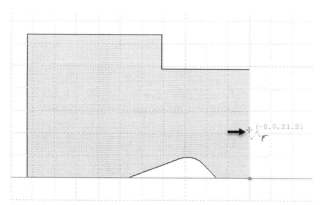

27. Move the pointer vertically upward, and then click to create the vertical line.

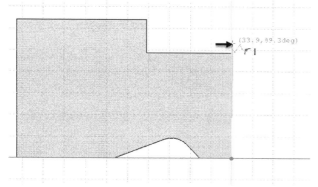

28. Move the pointer horizontally toward left, and then click.

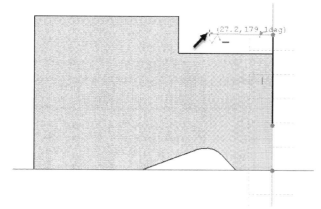

29. Move the vertically downward and click.

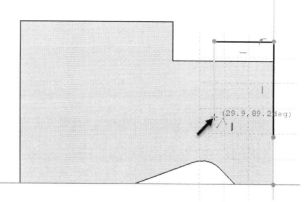

30. Right-click.
31. Click the **Arc** drop-down > **End points and rim point** on the **Sketcher geometries** toolbar.
32. Select the endpoints of the two vertical lines.

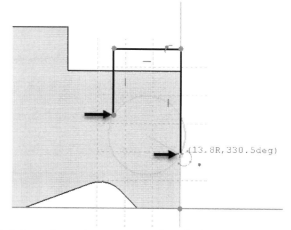

33. Move the pointer outward and click to create the arc.

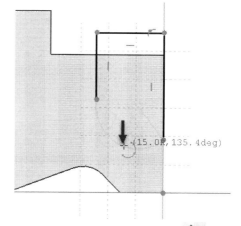

34. Click the **Constrain Tangent** icon on the **Sketcher constraints** toolbar.
35. Select the left vertical line and the arc.

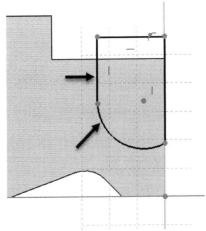

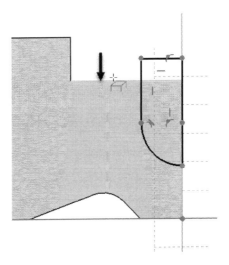

36. Click **OK** on the **Sketcher Constrain Substitution** message box.

37. Click the **Constrain point onto object** 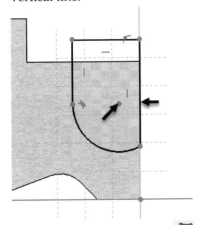 icon on the **Sketcher constraints** toolbar.

38. Select the center point of the circle and the right vertical line.

41. Click the **Constrain point onto object** icon on the **Sketcher constraints** toolbar.

42. Select the endpoint of the horizontal line and the external geometry.

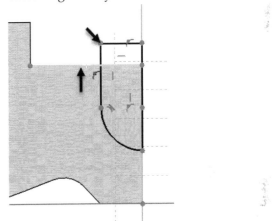

39. Click the **External geometry** icon on the **Sketcher geometries** toolbar.

40. Select the horizontal edge of the model, as shown.

43. Click the **Constraint diameter** drop-down > **Constrain arc or circle** on the **Sketcher constraints** toolbar.

44. Select the arc.

45. Type **0.8** and click **OK**.

46. Click the **Constrain vertical distance** icon on the **Sketcher constraints** toolbar.

47. Select the centerpoint of the arc and the sketch origin.

48. Type 1.4 in the **Length** box and click **OK**.

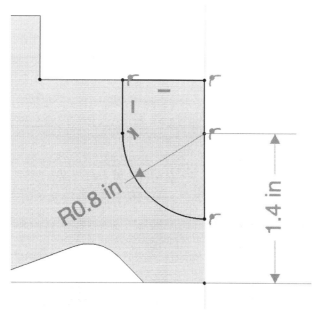

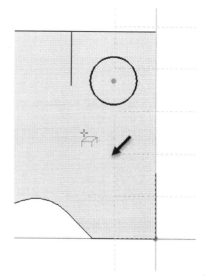

49. Click **Close** on the **Tasks** tab of the **Combo View** panel.

50. Click the **Pocket** icon on the **Part Design Modeling** toolbar; the sketch is selected automatically.

51. On the **Pocket parameters** dialog, select **Type > Dimension**.

52. Type **0.4** in the **Length** box.

53. Click **OK**.

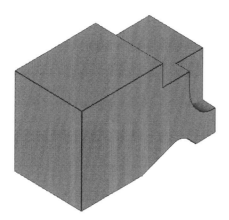

54. Select the flat face of the pocket feature.

55. Click the **Create Sketch** icon on the **Part Design Helper** toolbar.

56. Create a circle.

57. Click the **External geometry** icon on the **Sketcher geometries** toolbar.

58. Select the curved edge of the model, as shown.

59. Click the **Constrain symmetrical** icon on the **Sketcher constraints** toolbar.

60. Select the centerpoint of the curved edge.

61. Select the endpoint of the curved edge.

62. Select the centerpoint of the circle.

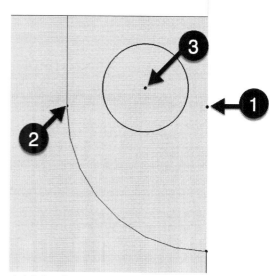

63. Add the diameter constraint to the circle.

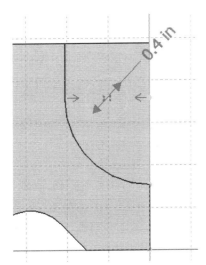

64. Click **Close** on the **Tasks** tab of the **Combo View** panel.

65. Click the **Pocket** icon on the **Part Design Modeling** toolbar; the sketch is selected automatically.

66. On the **Pocket parameters** dialog, select **Type > Through all**.

67. Click **OK**.

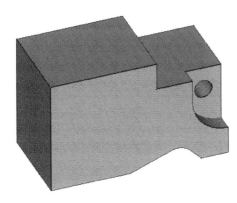

Creating the Pocket Feature on the left side

1. Click on the top face of the model.

2. Click the **Create Sketch** 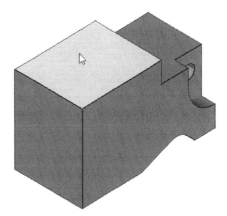 icon on the **Part Design Helper** toolbar.

3. Create a rectangle, as shown.

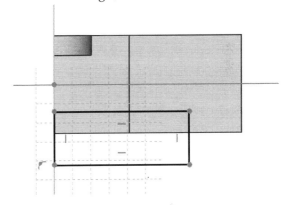

4. Create horizontal and vertical distance constraints, as shown.

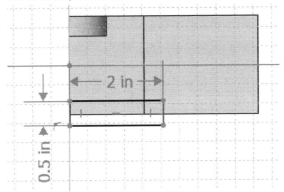

5. Click the **External geometry** icon on the **Sketcher geometries** toolbar.

6. Select the horizontal edge of the model, as shown.

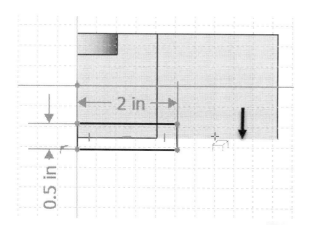

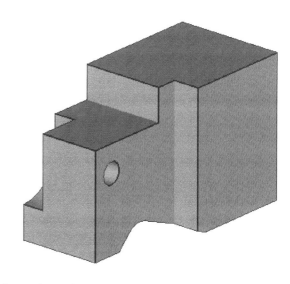

7. Click the **Constrain point onto object** icon on the **Sketcher constraints** toolbar.
8. Select the endpoint of the horizontal line and the external geometry.

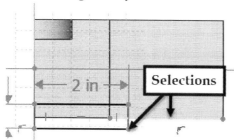

68. Click **Close** on the **Tasks** tab of the **Combo View** panel.
69. Click the **Pocket** icon on the **Part Design Modeling** toolbar; the sketch is selected automatically.
70. On the **Pocket parameters** dialog, select **Type > Through all**.
71. Click **OK**.

Creating the Angled Cut

1. Click on the front face of the model.

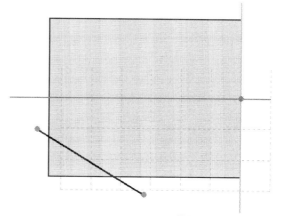

2. Click the **Create Sketch** icon on the **Part Design Helper** toolbar.
3. Create a line, as shown.

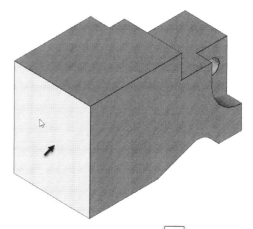

4. Click the **External geometry** icon on the

Sketcher geometries toolbar.

5. Select the horizontal and vertical edges of the model, as shown.

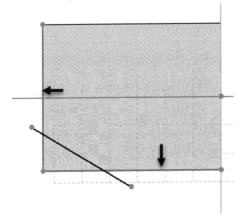

6. Click the **Constrain point onto object** 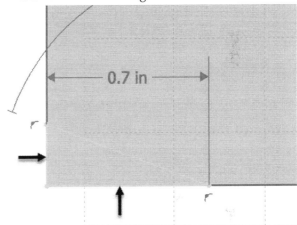 icon on the **Sketcher constraints** toolbar.
7. Select the endpoint of the line and the vertical edge.
8. Select the endpoint of the line and the horizontal edge.

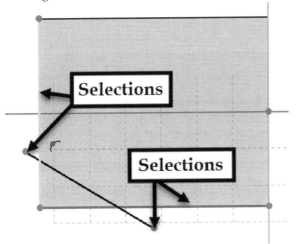

9. Create horizontal distance and angle constraints, as shown.

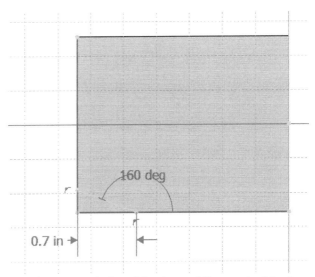

10. Create vertical and horizontal lines coincident with the extracted edges.

11. Click **Close** on the **Tasks** tab of the **Combo View** panel.

12. Click the **Pocket** icon on the **Part Design Modeling** toolbar; the sketch is selected automatically.

13. On the **Pocket parameters** dialog, select **Type > Through all**.

14. Click **OK**.

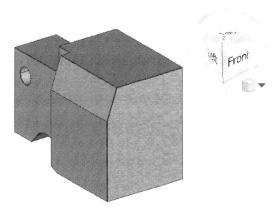

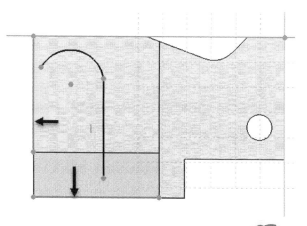

Creating the Pocket feature on the left

1. Click on the left face of the model.

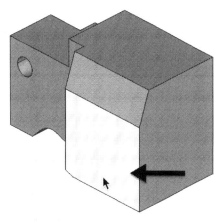

2. Click the **Create Sketch** icon on the **Part Design Helper** toolbar.
3. Create a line and arc, as shown.

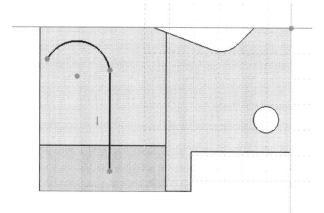

4. Click the **External geometry** icon on the **Sketcher geometries** toolbar.
5. Select the horizontal and vertical edges of the model, as shown.

6. Click the **Constrain point onto object** icon on the **Sketcher constraints** toolbar.
7. Select the endpoint of the arc and the vertical edge.
8. Select the endpoint of the line and the horizontal edge.

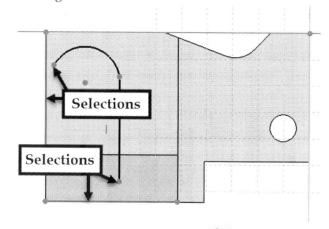

9. Click the **Constrain Tangent** icon on the **Sketcher constraints** toolbar.
10. Select the vertical line and the arc.
11. Create vertical and horizontal lines, as shown.

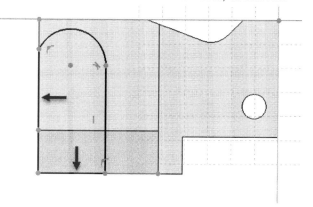

89

12. Click the **Constrain point onto object** 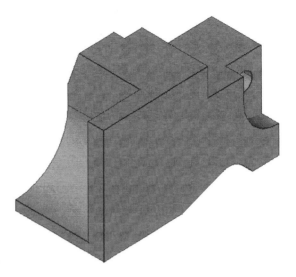 icon on the **Sketcher constraints** toolbar.

13. Select the centerpoint of the arc and the vertical edge.

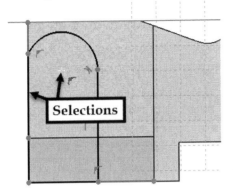

14. Create the radius and vertical distance constraints, as shown.

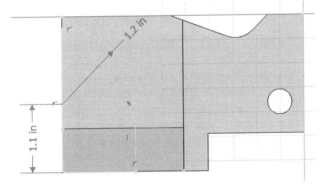

15. Click **Close** on the **Tasks** tab of the **Combo View** panel.

16. Click the **Pocket** icon on the **Part Design Modeling** toolbar; the sketch is selected automatically.

17. On the **Pocket parameters** dialog, select **Type > Dimension**.

18. Type **1.65** in the **Length** box.

19. Click **OK**.

Creating the Pocket feature on the right

1. Click on the right face of the model.

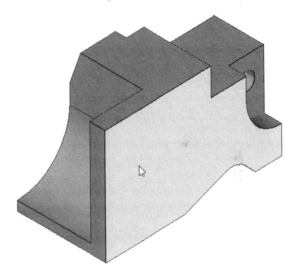

2. Click the **Create Sketch** icon on the **Part Design Helper** toolbar.

3. Create a circle.

4. Add the diameter and vertical distance constraint, as shown.

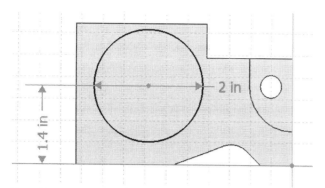

5. Create a vertical line, as shown.

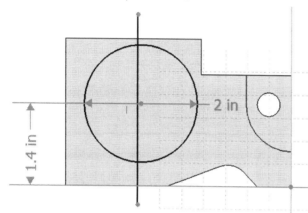

6. Click the **External geometry** icon on the **Sketcher geometries** toolbar.

7. Select the vertical and horizontal edges of the model, as shown.

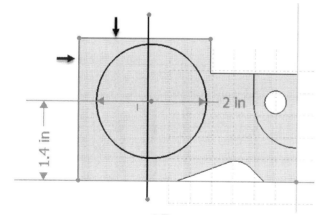

15. Click the **Trim Edge** icon on the **Sketcher geometries** toolbar.

16. Select the left side portion of the circle.

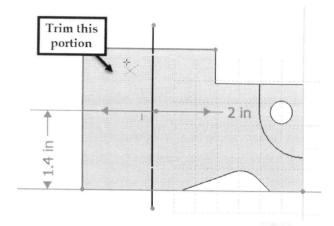

17. Click the **Constrain point onto object** icon on the **Sketcher constraints** toolbar.

18. Select endpoint the vertical line and the horizontal edge.

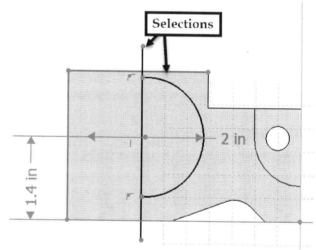

19. Trim the bottom and middle portions of the vertical line.

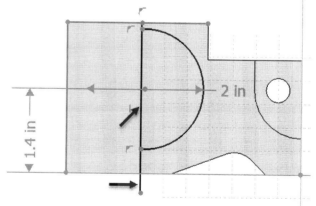

20. Click the **Arc** drop-down > **End points and rim point** on the **Sketcher geometries** toolbar.

21. Select the endpoint of the arc.
22. Move the pointer toward the left and click on the extracted edge.

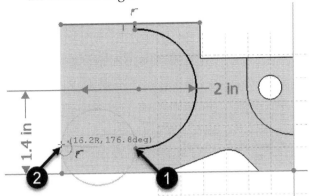

23. Move the pointer downward and click to create the arc.

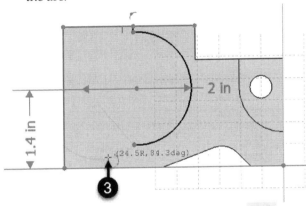

24. Click the **Constrain point onto object** icon on the **Sketcher constraints** toolbar.
25. Select the centerpoint of the new arc.
26. Select the extracted vertical edge.

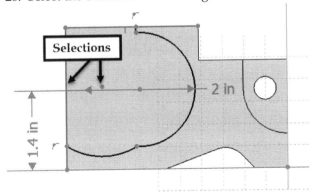

27. Right-click.
28. Select the centerpoints of the two arcs.

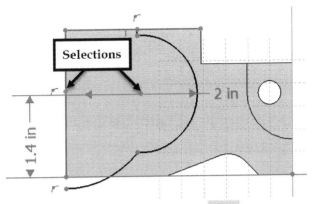

29. Click the **Constrain horizontal** icon on the **Sketcher constraints** toolbar.
30. Click the **Constrain equal** icon on the **Sketcher constraints** toolbar.
31. Select the two arcs to make their radius equal.

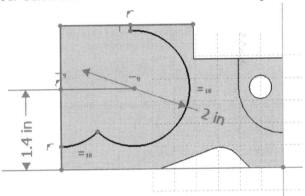

32. Create a horizontal distance constraint, as shown.

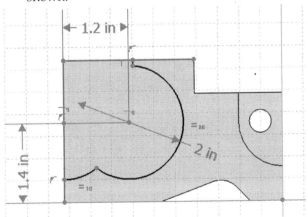

33. Select the center point and endpoint of the arc, as shown.

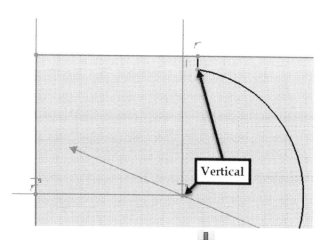

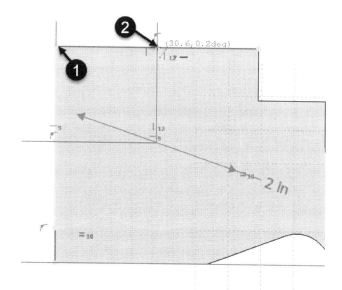

34. Click the **Constrain vertical** icon on the **Sketcher constraints** toolbar.

35. Click the **Create line** icon on the **Sketcher geometries** toolbar.

36. Select the endpoint of the small arc.

37. Move the pointer vertically upward and select the endpoint of the vertical edge.

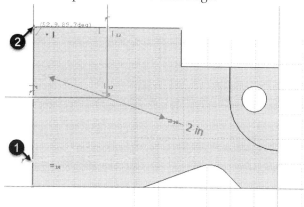

38. Select the endpoint of the vertical edge.

39. Move the pointer toward the right and select the endpoint of the vertical line.

40. Click **Close** on the **Tasks** tab of the **Combo View** panel.

41. Click the **Pocket** icon on the **Part Design Modeling** toolbar; the sketch is selected automatically.

42. On the **Pocket parameters** dialog, select **Type > Dimension**.

43. Type **0.5** in the **Length** box.

44. Click **OK**.

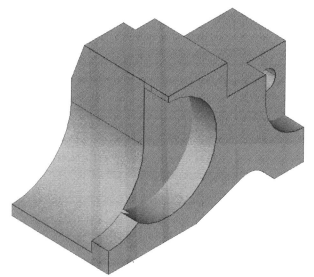

Adding the Pad Features

1. Click on the flat face of the pocket feature.

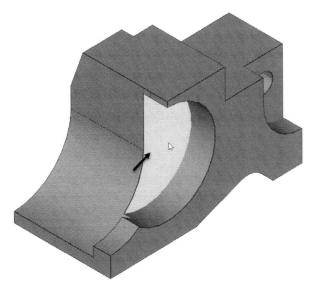

2. Click the **Create Sketch** icon on the **Part Design Helper** toolbar.
3. Create a circle and add the diameter constraint to it.

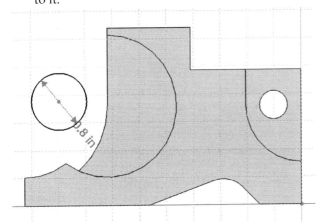

4. Click the **External geometry** icon on the **Sketcher geometries** toolbar.
5. Select the circular edge of the model.
6. Select the vertical and circular edge, as shown.

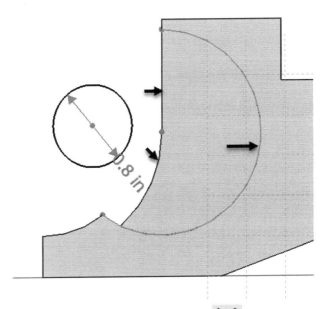

7. Click the **Constrain coincident** icon on the **Sketcher constraints** toolbar.
8. Select the centerpoint of the circle and the curved edge.

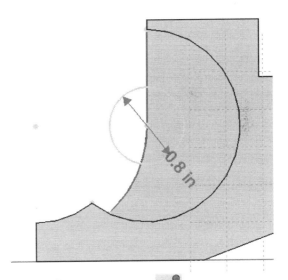

9. Click the **Create Line** icon on the **Sketcher geometries** toolbar.
10. Specify the start and endpoint of the line, as shown.

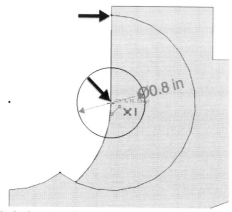

11. Click the **Arc** drop-down > **Center and endpoints** on the **Sketcher geometries** toolbar.

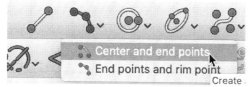

12. Specify the center, start, and endpoints of the arc, as shown.

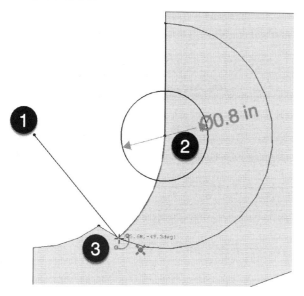

13. Click the **Trim Edge** icon on the **Sketcher geometries** toolbar.
14. Select the portions of the sketch to be trimmed, as shown.

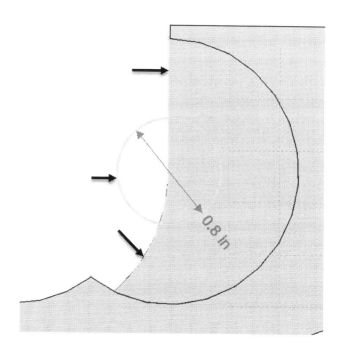

15. Click the **Constrain vertical** icon on the **Sketcher constraints** toolbar.
16. Select the line, as shown.

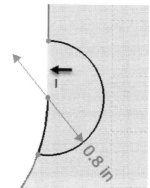

17. Click **Close** on the **Tasks** tab of the **Combo View** panel.
18. Click the **Pad** icon on the **Part Design Modeling** toolbar; the sketch is selected automatically.
19. Type **0.2** in the **Length** box.
20. Click **OK**.

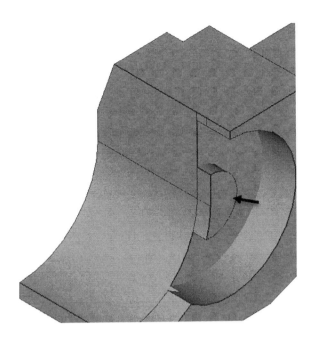

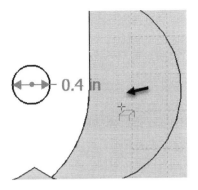

21. Click on the face of the pad feature, as shown.

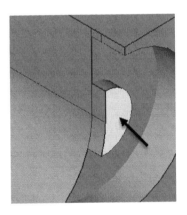

22. Click the **Create Sketch** icon on the **Part Design Helper** toolbar.
23. Create a circle and add the diameter constraint to it.
24. Click the **External geometry** icon on the **Sketcher geometries** toolbar.
25. Select the circular edge of the model, as shown.

26. Click the **Constrain coincident** icon on the **Sketcher constraints** toolbar.
27. Select the centerpoint of the circle and the curved edge.
28. Click **Close** on the **Tasks** tab of the **Combo View** panel.
29. Click the **Pad** icon on the **Part Design Modeling** toolbar; the sketch is selected automatically.
30. On the **Pad parameters** dialog, select **Type > Up To face**.
31. Select the right face of the model, as shown.

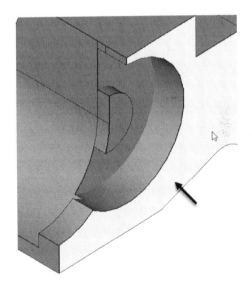

32. Click **OK**.

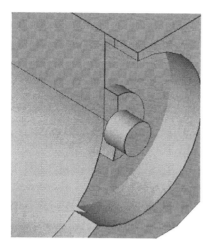

33. Save and close the model.

TUTORIAL 9

In this tutorial, you construct the model shown in the figure.

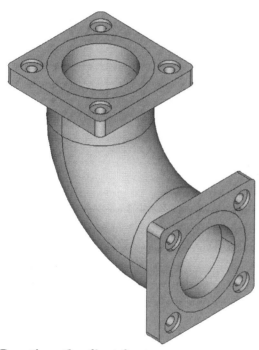

Creating the first feature

1. Open the FreeCAD application.
2. Click **File > New** on the Menu bar.
3. Select the **Part Design** option from the **Workbenches** drop-down.
4. Click the **Create sketch** icon on the **Part Design Helper** toolbar, and then select the XZ Plane.

5. Click **OK** to start the sketch.
6. Click the **Polyline** icon on the **Sketcher geometries** toolbar.
7. Create a vertical and horizontal lines connected to each other, as shown.

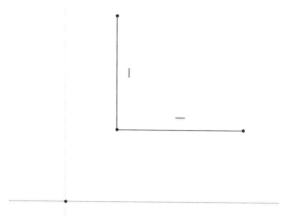

8. Click the **Fillet** drop-down > **Sketch Fillet** on the **Sketcher geometries** toolbar.
9. Select the vertical and horizontal lines; a fillet created at the intersection of the two lines.

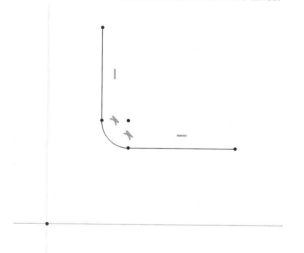

10. Click **Sketcher constraints** toolbar > **Constrain vertical distance** (or) click **Sketch > Sketcher constraints > Constrain vertical distance** on the menu bar.
11. Select the vertical line.
12. Enter **5.9** in the **Length** box of the **Insert Length** dialog and click **OK**.

13. Click **Sketcher constraints** toolbar > **Constrain horizontal distance** 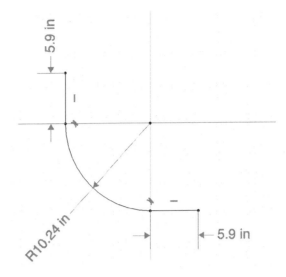 (or) click **Sketch >
Sketcher constraints > Constrain horizontal distance** on the menu bar.
14. Select the horizontal line.
15. Enter **5.9** in the **Length** box of the **Insert Length** dialog and click the **OK** button.
16. On the **Sketcher constraints** toolbar, click **Constrain diameter** drop-down > **Constrain radius** icon.
17. Select the circle and type **10.24** in the **Radius** box of the **Change Radius** dialog.
18. Click **OK**.
19. Click the **Constrain Coincident** icon on the **Sketcher constraints** toolbar.
20. Select the origin point of the sketch
21. Select the center point of the fillet.

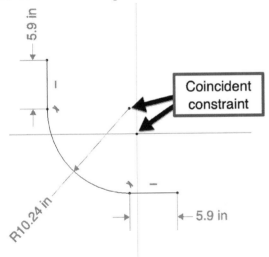

22. Click **Close** on the **Tasks** tab of the **Combo View** panel.

23. On the **Part Design Helper** toolbar, click the **Create a new datum plane** icon.
24. Select the horizontal line of the sketch.
25. Select the endpoint of the horizontal line.
26. Select the **Normal to edge** option from the **Attachment mode** section of the **Combo View** panel.
27. Click **OK**.

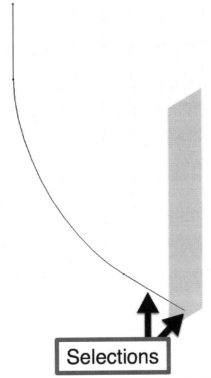

28. Click the **Create Sketch** icon the **Part Design Helper** toolbar.

29. Select the newly created datum plane and click **OK** on the **Combo View** panel.

30. Click the **Create Circle** 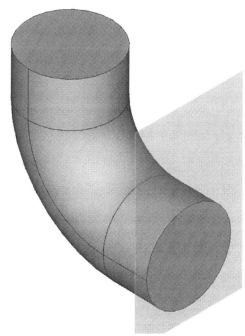 on the **Sketcher geometries** toolbar.

31. Click on the origin.

32. Move the pointer outward and click to create a circle.

33. On the **Sketcher constraints** toolbar, click the **Constrain diameter** drop-down > **Constrain diameter** icon.

34. Select the circle and type **11.41** in the **Diameter** box on the **Change diameter** dialog.

35. Make sure that the center of the circle and origin point are coincident.

36. Click **OK**.

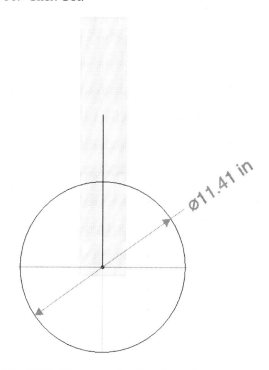

37. Click **Close** on the **Combo View** panel.

38. On the **Part Design Modelling** toolbar, click the **Sweep** icon.

39. Select Sketch001 from the **Select feature** and click **OK** on the **Combo View** panel.

40. Click on the **Object** button of **Path** option and select the first sketch.

41. Click **OK** on the **Combo View** panel.

42. Select the datum plane from the graphics window.

43. On the **Combo View** panel, set the **Visibility** value to **false**.

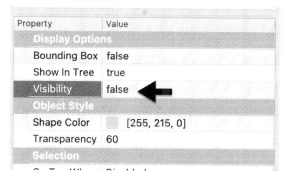

44. Click in the graphics window to deselect the datum plane.

Creating the Shell feature

1. Press **Ctrl** and select the faces, as shown.

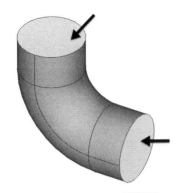

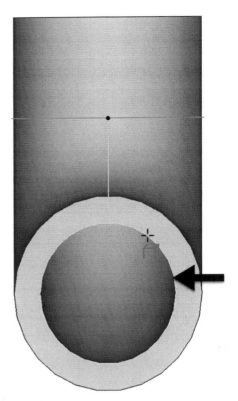

2. Click the **Thickness** tool on the **Part Design Modeling** toolbar.
3. Enter **1.575** in the **Thickness** box under the **Thickness Parameter** section.
4. Check **Make thickness inwards** option.
5. Click **OK** on the **Combo View** panel.
6. Select the flat face of the AdditivePipe, as shown.

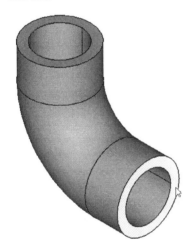

Creating the Flanges

1. Click **Create new Sketch** icon on the **Part Design Helper toolbar**.

2. Click the **External Geometry** icon on the **Sketcher geometries** toolbar.

3. Select the inner circular edge of the model, as shown.

4. Expand the **Sketcher geometries** toolbar and click the **Polygon** drop-down > **Square**.

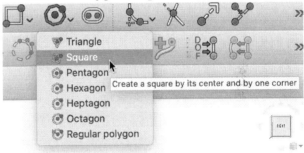

5. Select the centerpoint of the circular edge.
6. Move the pointer outward and click to create a square. Next, Press **Esc**.

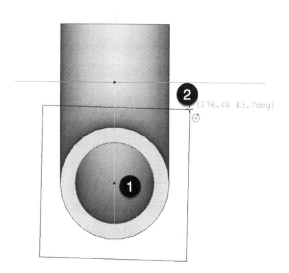

7. On the **Sketcher constraints** toolbar, click the **Horizontal constraint** icon.
8. Select the top horizontal line, as shown.

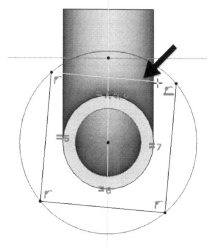

9. Click **Sketcher constraints** toolbar > **Constrain horizontal distance** (or) click **Sketch >** **Sketcher constraints > Constrain horizontal distance** on the menu bar.
10. Select the top horizontal line.
11. Enter **14.173** in the **Length** box of the **Insert Length** dialog and click the **OK** button.

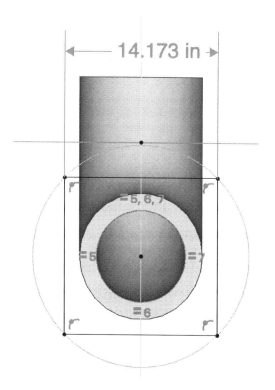

12. Click the **Create Circle** on the **Sketcher geometries** toolbar.
13. Select the centerpoint of the circular edge.
14. Move the pointer outward and click on the inner circular edge.

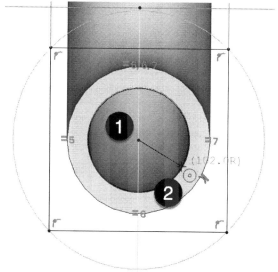

15. Click **Close** on the **Combo View** panel.
16. On the **Part Design Modeling** toolbar, click the **Pad** icon.

17. Type **1.969** in the **Length** box of the **Pad Parameters** dialog.
18. Check the **Reversed** option and click **OK**.

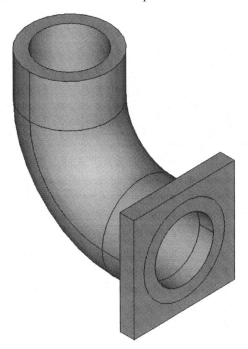

19. Press and hold the Ctrl key and select the edges of the model, as shown.

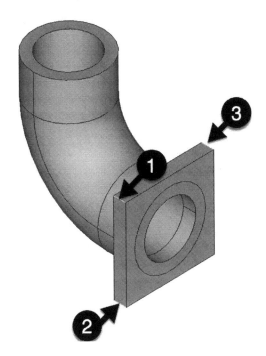

20. On the **Part Design Modeling** toolbar, click the **Fillet** icon.

21. Click the **Add** button on the **Fillet Parameters** dialog.
22. Press and hold the middle and right mouse buttons, and then drag the pointer; the model is rotated.
23. Select the edge of the model, as shown.

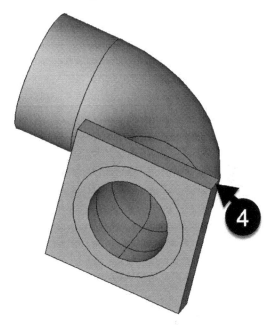

24. Type **0.787** in the **Radius** box.
25. Click **OK**.
26. Click the **ViewCube** drop-down, and then select the **Isometric** option.

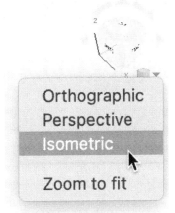

27. Select the flat face of the **Pad** feature, as shown.

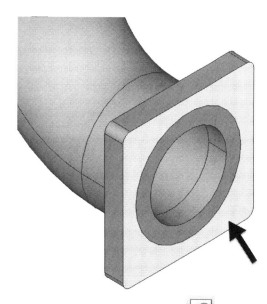

28. Click **Create new Sketch** icon on the **Part Design Helper toolbar**.

29. Click the **External Geometry** icon on the **Sketcher geometries** toolbar.

30. Select the horizontal and vertical edges, as shown.

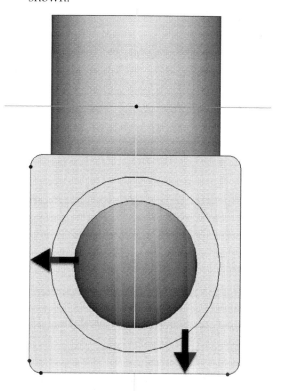

31. Click the **Create Circle** on the **Sketcher**

geometries toolbar.

32. Create a circle, as shown.

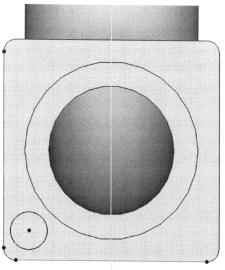

33. Click **Sketcher constraints** toolbar > **Constrain vertical distance** (or) click **Sketch >** **Sketcher constraints > Constrain vertical distance** on the menu bar.

34. Select the centerpoint of the circle.

35. Select the left endpoint of the horizontal edge, as shown.

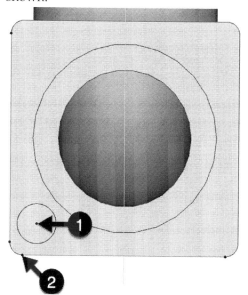

36. Enter **1.969** in the **Length** box of the **Insert Length** dialog and click **OK**.

37. Click **Sketcher constraints** toolbar > **Constrain horizontal distance** (or) click **Sketch >**

Sketcher constraints > Constrain horizontal distance on the menu bar.

38. Select the centerpoint of the circle.
39. Select the lower endpoint of the vertical edge, as shown.
40. Enter **1.969** in the **Length** box of the **Insert Length** dialog and click the **OK** button.

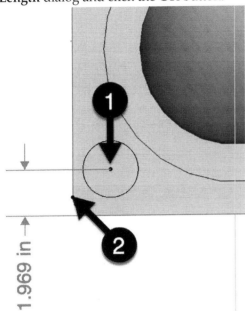

41. Click **Close** on the **Combo View** panel.
42. Click the **Hole** icon on the **Part Design Modeling** toolbar.
43. Type **1.181 in** in the **Diameter** box.
44. Select **Depth > Dimension**.
45. Type 1.969 in the **Depth** box located next to the **Depth** drop-down.
46. On the **Hole Parameters** section, under **Hole cut**, select **Type > Counterbore**.
47. Type **2.362** in the **Diameter** box.
48. Type **0.394** in the **Depth** box.
49. Under **Drill point**, select **Type > Flat**.

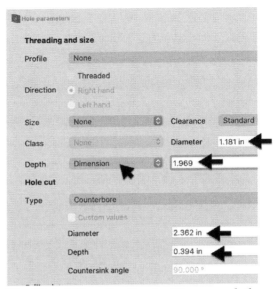

50. Click **OK** on the **Combo View** panel; the counterbore hole is created.

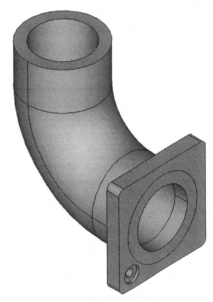

51. Select the **Hole** feature from the **Model** tab of the **Combo View** panel.
52. Click the **MultiTransform** tool on the **Part Design Modeling** toolbar.
53. In the **MultiTransform parameters** section, right click in the **Transformations** section, and then select **Add linear pattern**.

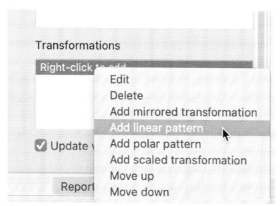

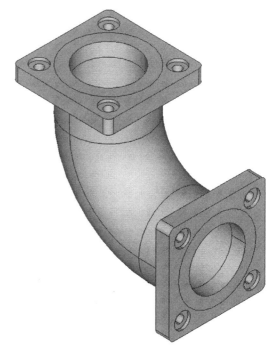

54. Select the **Horizontal sketch axis** from the **Direction** drop-down.
55. Type **10.235** in the **Length** box.
56. Type-in **2** in the **Occurrences** box.
57. Right click in the **Transformations** section, and then select **Add linear pattern**.
58. Select the **Vertical sketch axis** from the **Direction** drop-down.
59. Type **10.235** in the **Length** box.
60. Type-in **2** in the **Occurrences** box.
61. Click **OK** to create the multi transformation pattern.

TUTORIAL 10

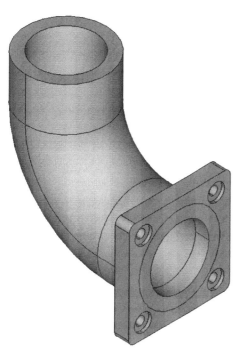

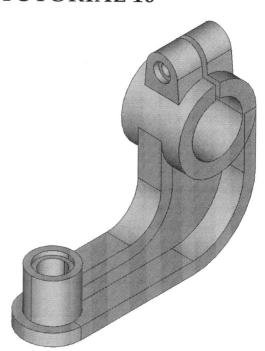

62. Likewise, create another flange on the other end of the AdditivePipe, as shown.

Creating the first feature

1. Open the FreeCAD application.
2. Click **File > New** on the Menu bar.
3. Select the **Part Design** option from the **Workbenches** drop-down.
4. Click the **Create sketch**  icon on the **Part**

Design Helper toolbar, and then select the YZ Plane.

5. Click **OK** to start the sketch.

6. Click the **Create circle** icon on the **Sketcher geometries** toolbar.

7. On the **Sketcher constrain** toolbar, click the **Constrain Diameter** drop-down > **Constrain Diameter** ∅.

8. Select the circle and type in **3.937** in the **Diameter** box on the **Change diameter** dialog.

9. Click **OK**.

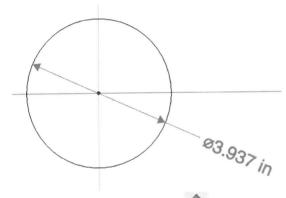

10. Click the **Leave Sketch** icon on the **Part Design Helper toolbar**.

11. On the **Part Design Modelling** toolbar, click **Pad** icon.

12. Type-in **2.953** in the **Length** box.

13. Check the **Symmetric to plane** option and click **OK**.

Creating the Second feature

1. Click the **Create sketch** icon on the **Part Design Helper** toolbar, and then select the YZ Plane.

2. Click **OK** on the **Combo View** panel.

3. Create a sketch using the **Polyline** and **Fillet** tools, as shown.

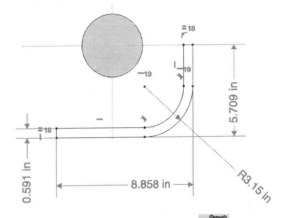

4. Click the **External Geometry** icon on the **Sketcher geometries** toolbar.

5. Select the circular edge of the model, as shown.

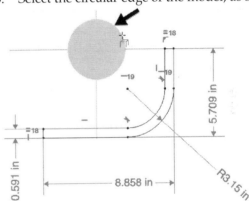

6. On the **Sketcher constrain** toolbar, click the **Tangent Constraint** icon.

7. Select the circular edge and the right vertical line.

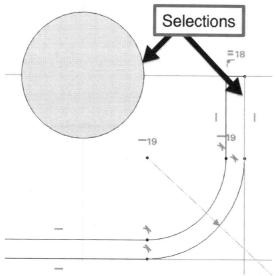

8. Click **Close** on the **Tasks** tab of the **Combo View** panel.

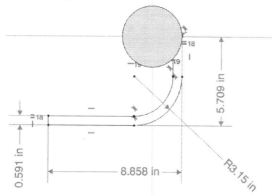

9. Click **Model** tab on the **Combo View** panel.
10. On the **Part Design Modelling** toolbar, click **Pad** icon.
11. Type-in **2.953** in the **Length** box.
12. Check the **Symmetric to plane** option and click **OK**.

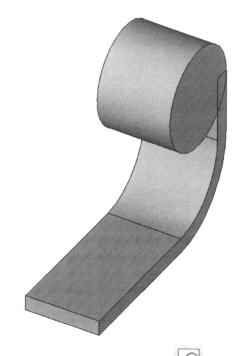

13. Click the **Create sketch** icon on the **Part Design Helper** toolbar, and then select the YZ Plane.
14. Click **OK** on the **Combo View** panel.
15. Create a sketch using the **Polyline** and **Fillet** tools, as shown.

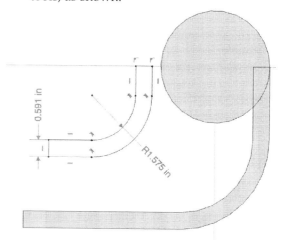

16. Click the **External Geometry** icon on the **Sketcher geometries** toolbar.
17. Select the circular, horizontal and vertical edges of the model, as shown.

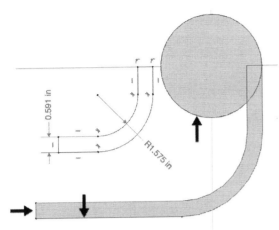

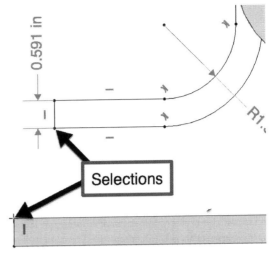

18. On the **Sketcher constrain** toolbar, click the

    Tangent Constraint icon.

19. Select the circular edge and the left vertical line.

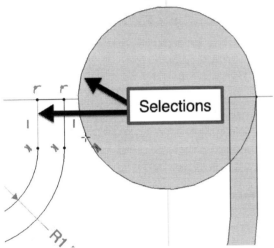

20. On the **Sketcher constrain** toolbar, click the

    Vertical Constraint icon.

21. Select the lower end point of the vertical line, as shown.

22. Select anyone of the vertices of the vertical edge, as shown.

23. Click **Sketcher constraints** toolbar > **Constrain vertical distance** (or) click **Sketch > Sketcher constraints > Constrain vertical distance** on the menu bar.

24. Select the top endpoint of the vertical line, as shown

25. Select the left endpoint of the horizontal edge, as shown.

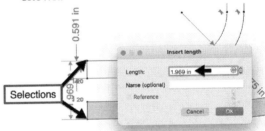

26. Type **1.969** in the **Length** box and click **OK**.

27. Click **Close** on the **Combo View** panel.

28. On the **Part Design Modeling** toolbar, click the

    Pad icon.

29. Type **1.181** in the **Length** box of the **Pad Parameters** dialog.

30. Check the **Symmetric to plane** option and click **OK**.

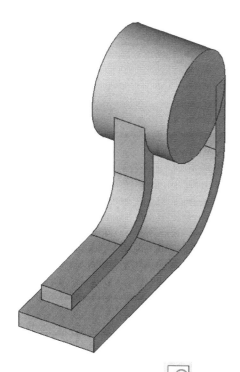

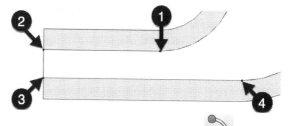

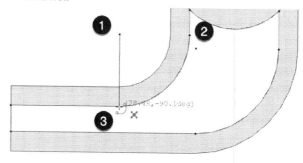

31. Click the **Create sketch** 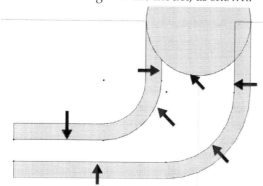 icon on the **Part Design Helper** toolbar, and then select the YZ Plane.

32. Click **OK** on the **Combo View** panel.

33. Click the **External Geometry** icon on the **Sketcher geometries** toolbar.

34. Select the edges of the model, as shown.

35. Click the **View section** icon on the **Part Design Helper** toolbar.

36. Click the **Create Polyline** icon on the Sketcher geometries toolbar.

37. Select the vertices of the external geometry in the sequence shown in figure.

38. Click the **Create arc by center** icon on the **Sketcher geometries** toolbar.

39. Select the center point of the curved edge, as shown.

40. Select the two vertices of the curved edge, as shown.

41. Likewise, create two more arcs by specifying the center, start, and end points, as shown.

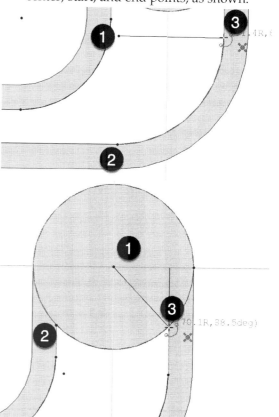

42. Click the **Create line** 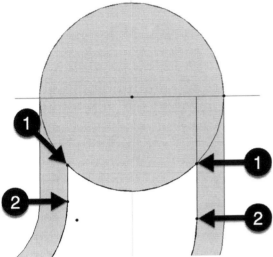 icon on the **Sketcher geometries** toolbar.
43. Select the vertices of the vertical edges, as shown.

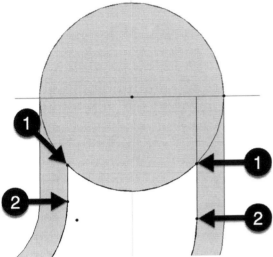

44. Click **Close** on the **Combo View** panel.
45. On the **Part Design Modeling** toolbar, click the **Pad** icon.
46. Type **0.787** in the **Length** box of the **Pad Parameters** dialog.
47. Check the **Symmetric to plane** option and click **OK**.

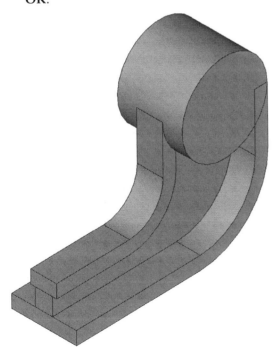

48. Press and hold the right and middle mouse button and drag the pointer upward.
49. Select the bottom flat face.

50. Click **Create new Sketch** icon on the **Part Design Helper toolbar**.
51. Click the **External Geometry** icon on the **Sketcher geometries** toolbar.
52. Select the edge of the model, as shown.

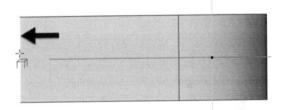

53. Click the **Create arc by three points** icon on the **Sketcher geometries** toolbar.
54. Select the two vertices of the edge, as shown.
55. Move the pointer towards left and click.

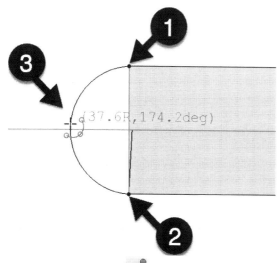

56. Click the **Create line**  icon on the **Sketcher geometries** toolbar.
57. Select the vertices of the vertical edge, as shown.

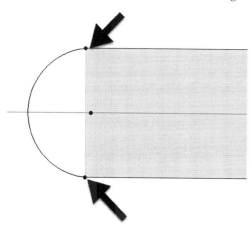

58. On the **Sketcher constrain** toolbar, click the

    Constrain point onto object icon.
59. Select the centerpoint of the arc and the vertical line, as shown.

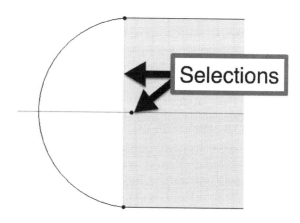

60. Click **Close** on the **Combo View** panel.
61. On the **Part Design Modeling** toolbar, click the

    Pad icon.
62. Select **Type > Up to face** on the Pad parameters dialog.
63. Select the horizontal face of the model, as shown.

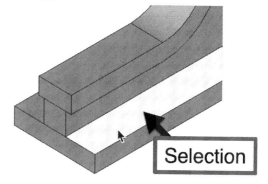

64. Click **OK**.

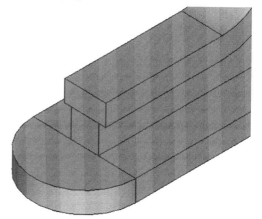

Creating the third feature

1. Select the horizontal face of the model, as shown.

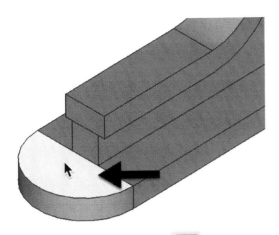

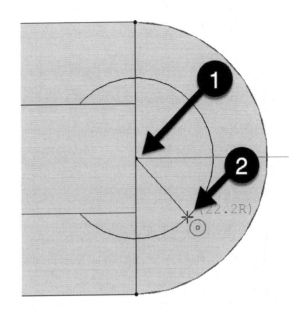

2. Click **Create new Sketch** icon on the **Part Design Helper toolbar**.

3. Click the **External Geometry** icon on the **Sketcher geometries** toolbar.

4. Select the circular edge of the model, as shown.

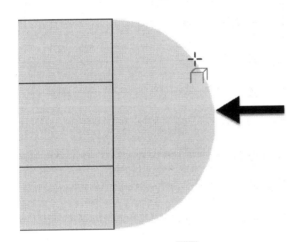

5. Click the **Create circle** icon on the **Sketcher geometry** toolbar.

6. Click on the centerpoint of the curved edge.

7. Move the pointer outward and click to create the circle.

8. On the **Sketcher constraints** toolbar, click the **Constrain radius** drop-down and select **Constrain diameter** .

9. Select the circle and type-in **2.165** in the **Diameter** box on the **Change Diameter** dialog.

10. Click **OK**.

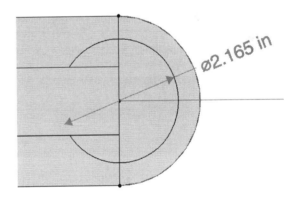

11. Click **Close** on the **Combo View** panel.

12. On the **Part Design Modeling** toolbar, click the **Pad** icon.

13. Type **1.969** in the **Length** box of the **Pad Parameters** dialog.

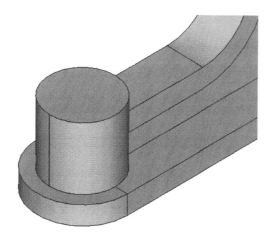

Creating the fourth feature

1. Click the **Create sketch** 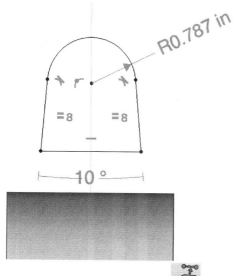icon on the **Part Design Helper** toolbar, and then select the XZ Plane.
2. Click **OK** to start the sketch.
3. Create the sketch, as shown.

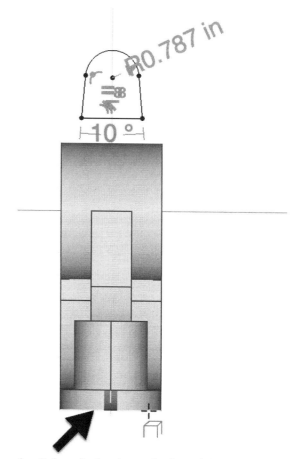

4. Click the **External Geometry** icon on the **Sketcher geometries** toolbar.
5. Select the bottom horizontal edge of the model, as shown.

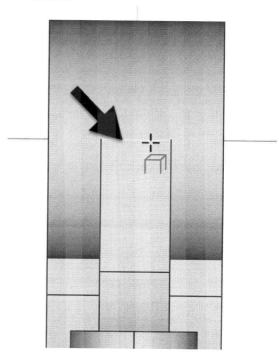

6. Select the horizontal edge of the model, as shown.

113

7. Click the **View section** icon on the **Part Design Helper** toolbar.
8. On the **Sketcher constrain** toolbar, click the **Constrain point onto object** icon.
9. Select the endpoint of the horizontal line, as shown.
10. Select the external geometry, as shown.

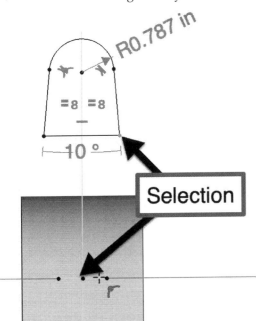

11. Click **Sketcher constraints** toolbar > **Constrain vertical distance** (or) click **Sketch > Sketcher constraints > Constrain vertical distance** on the menu bar.
12. Select the centerpoint of the arc.
13. Select the endpoint of the bottom external geometry.

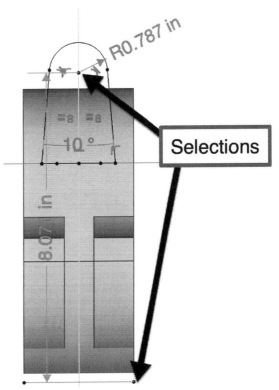

14. Enter **8.071** in the **Length** box of the **Insert Length** dialog and click **OK**.
15. Click **Close** on the **Combo View** panel.
16. On the **Part Design Modeling** toolbar, click the **Pad** icon.
17. Type **2.756** in the **Length** box of the **Pad Parameters** dialog.
18. Check the **Symmetric to plane** option and click **OK**.

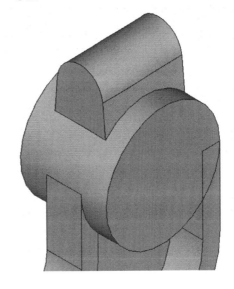

Creating Holes

1. Select the horizontal face of the model, as shown.

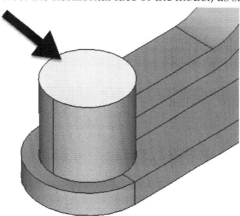

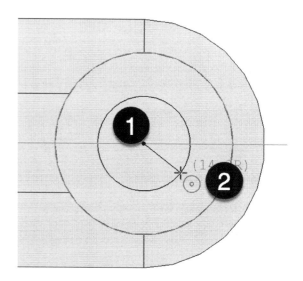

2. Click **Create new Sketch** 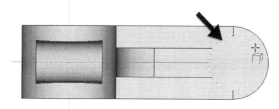 icon on the **Part Design Helper toolbar**.

3. Click the **External Geometry** icon on the **Sketcher geometries** toolbar.

4. Select the circular edge of the model, as shown.

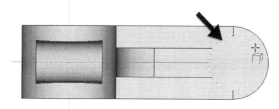

5. Click the **Create circle** icon on the **Sketcher geometry** toolbar.

6. Click on the centerpoint of the curved edge.

7. Move the pointer outward and click to create the circle.

8. Click **Close** on the **Combo View** panel.

9. Click the **Hole** icon on the **Part Design Modeling** toolbar.

10. Type **1.181** in the **Diameter** box.

11. Select **Depth > Through All**.

12. On the **Hole Parameters** section, under **Hole cut**, select **Type > Counterbore**.

13. Type **1.575** in the **Diameter** box.

14. Type **0.197** in the **Depth** box.

15. Click **OK** on the **Combo View** panel; the counterbore hole is created.

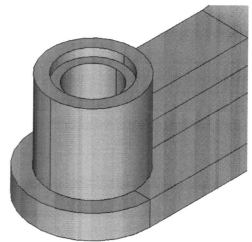

16. Likewise, create a simple and counterbored hole, as shown.

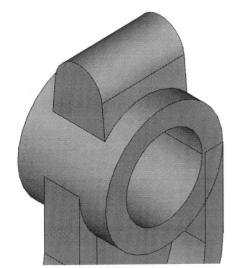

Hole diameter: 2.559 in
Depth: Through all

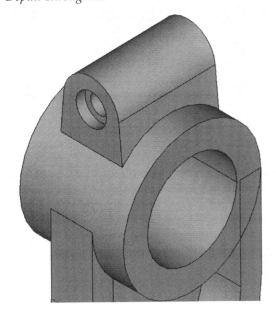

Diameter: 0.551 in
Depth: Through all
Type: Counterbore
Counterbore Diameter: 0.866 in
Depth: 0.260 in

Creating the Pocket feature

1. Select the flat face of the model, as shown.

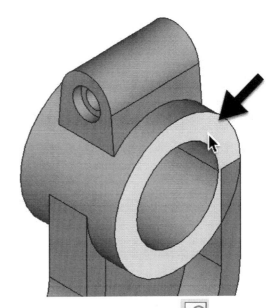

2. Click **Create new Sketch** 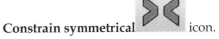 icon on the **Part Design Helper toolbar**.

3. Create a rectangle and dimensions to it, as shown.

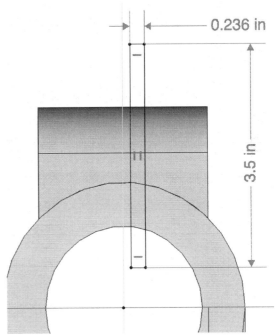

4. On the **Sketcher constrain** toolbar, click the

   Constrain symmetrical icon.

5. Select the endpoints of the horizontal line, as shown.

6. Select the sketch origin.

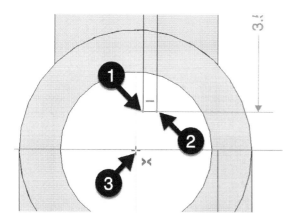

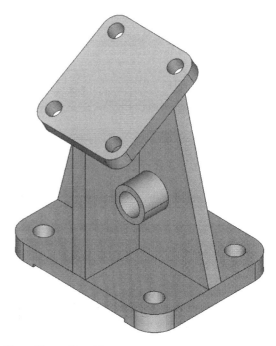

7. Click **Close** on the **Combo View** panel.
8. On the **Part Design Modeling** toolbar, click the

   Pocket ⬚ icon.

9. Select **Type > Through all**, and then click **OK**.

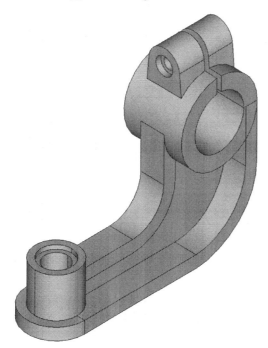

TUTORIAL 11

In this tutorial, you create the model shown in the figure:

Creating the Base

1. Open the FreeCAD application.
2. Click **File > New** on the Menu bar.
3. Select the **Part Design** option from the **Workbenches** drop-down.
4. On the Menu bar, click **Edit > Preferences**.
5. Click the **Units** tab on the **Preferences** dialog.
6. Select **User system > Imperial decimal**.
7. Type **3** in the **Number of decimals** box.
8. Click **OK**.

9. Click the **Create sketch** ⬚ icon on the **Part Design Helper** toolbar, and then select the XY Plane.
10. Click **OK** to start the sketch.
11. Click the **Create Rectangle** icon on the **Sketcher geometries** toolbar.
12. Create a sketch, as shown.

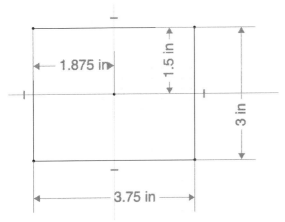

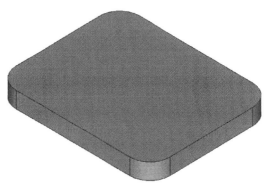

13. Click **Close** on the **Combo View** panel.
14. Click the **Pad** icon on the **Part Design Modelling** toolbar.
15. Select **Type > Dimension** on the **Pad parameters** section.
16. Type-in **0.38** in in the **Length** box.
17. Click **OK** on the **Combo View** panel.

18. Select the front right edge, as shown.

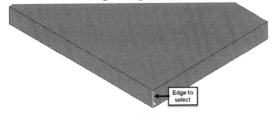

19. Click the **Create fillet** icon on the **Part Design Modeling** toolbar.
20. Click the **Add** button on the **Fillet parameters** section.
21. Select the front left edge.
22. Likewise, select the back vertical edges of the pad features.
23. Type-in **0.50** in in the **Radius** box.
24. Click **OK** on the **Combo View** panel.

25. Click on the top face of the **Pad** feature and click **Create Sketch** on the **Part Design Helper toolbar**.

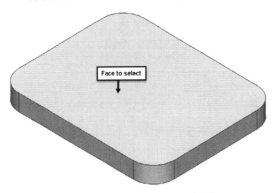

26. Click the **External geometry** icon on the **Sketcher geometries** toolbar.
27. Select the top right arc of the Pad feature, as shown.
28. Likewise, select the remaining arcs of the pad feature, as shown.

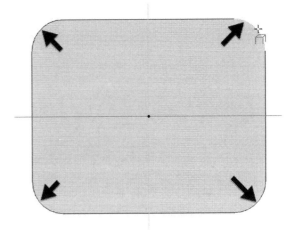

29. Press **Esc** to deactivate the tool.
30. On the **Sketcher geometries** toolbar, click the **Create circle** icon.
31. Select the centerpoint of the circular edge.

118

32. Move the pointer outward and click.

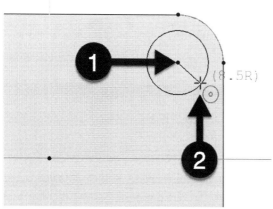

33. Likewise, create three more circles, as shown.

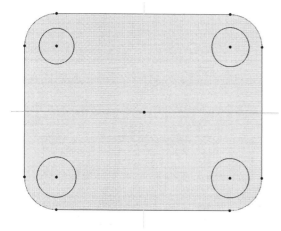

34. Click **Close** on the **Combo View** panel.
35. On the **Part Design Modelling** toolbar, click the **Hole** icon.
36. Select **Depth > Through all**.
37. Type **0.38** in the **Diameter** box.
38. Click **OK** on the **Combo View** panel.

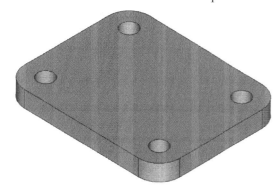

Creating the Rib
1. On the **Part Design Helper toolbar**, click the **Create Sketch** icon.

2. Select **XZ-Plane** on the **Select feature** and click **OK**.
3. Click the **External geometry** icon on the **Sketcher geometries** toolbar.
4. Select the edges of the model, as shown.

5. On the **Sketcher geometries** toolbar, click the **Create Polyline** icon.
6. Select the right endpoint of the external geometry, as shown.

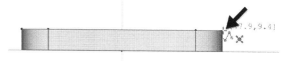

7. Specify the second and third points of the polyline, as shown.
8. Select the left point of the external geometry, as shown.

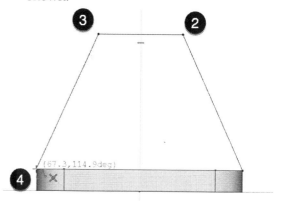

9. Move the pointer toward right and select the start point of the polyline.

10. Add dimensional constraints to the sketch, and

then click **Leave Sketch** 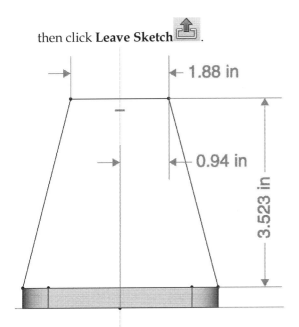.

11. On the **Part Design Modeling** toolbar, click the **Pad** icon.

12. Type **0.31** in the **Length** box of the **Pad Parameters** dialog.

13. Check the **Symmetric to plane** option and click **OK**.

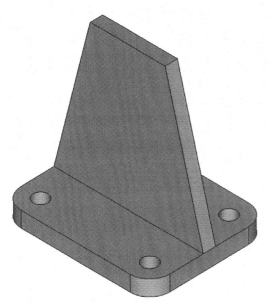

14. Click on the horizontal face of the model, as shown.

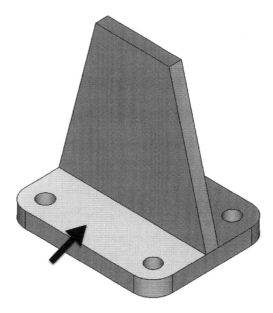

15. Click **Create Sketch** on the **Part Design Helper** toolbar.

16. Click the **External geometry** icon on the **Sketcher geometries** toolbar.

17. Select the horizontal edges of the model, as shown.

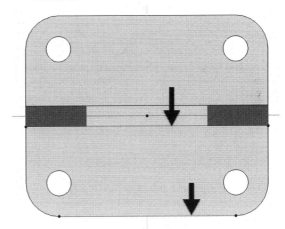

18. Specify the first and second corners of the rectangle of the two external geometries, as shown.

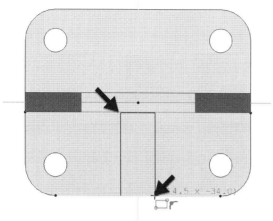

19. Add dimensional constraints to the rectangle, and then click **Leave Sketch** .

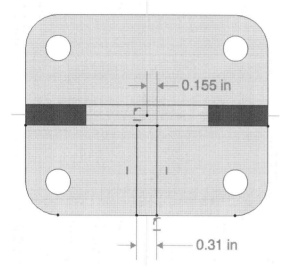

20. On the **Part Design Modeling** toolbar, click the **Pad** icon.
21. Select **Type > Up to face** on the **Pad parameters** dialog.
22. Select the horizontal face of the model, as shown.

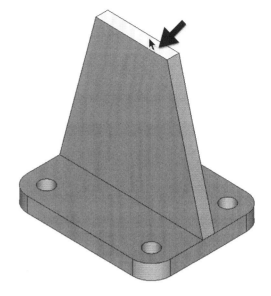

23. Click **OK**.

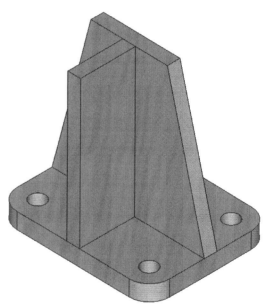

24. On the **Part Design Helper** toolbar, click the **Create Sketch** icon.
25. Select **YZ-Plane** on the **Select feature** and click **OK**.
26. Click the **View section** icon on the **Part Design Helper** toolbar.
27. On the **Sketcher geometries** toolbar, click the **Create Polyline** icon.
28. Create a closed sketch, as shown.

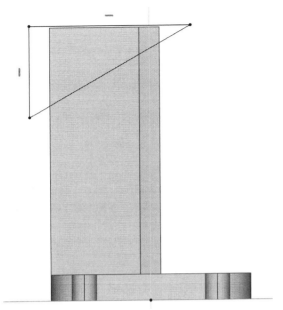

29. Add dimensions to the sketch, as shown.

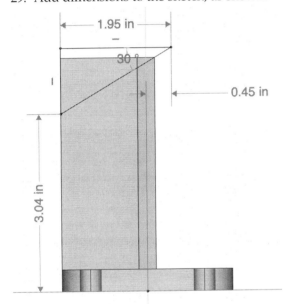

1.95 in

30°

0.45 in

3.04 in

30. Click **Close** on the **Combo View** panel.
31. On the **Part Design Modelling** toolbar, click the **Pocket** icon.
32. Select **Type > Through all** under the **Pad parameters** section.
33. Check the **Symmetric to plane** option.
34. Click **OK** on the **Combo View** panel.

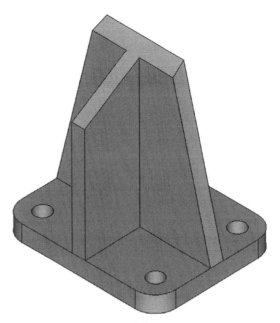

Creating the Third feature

1. Click on the inclined face of the model, as shown.

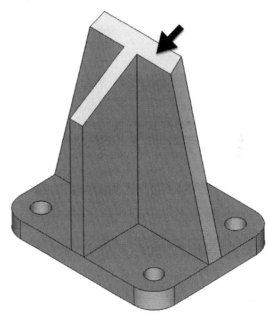

2. On the **Part Design Helper** toolbar, click the **Create Sketch** icon.
3. Create the rectangle and add dimensions to it, as shown.

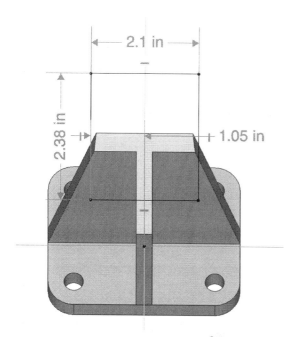

4. Click the **External geometry** icon on the **Sketcher geometries** toolbar.

5. Select the horizontal edges of the model, as shown.

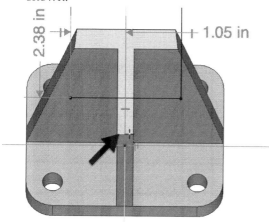

6. On the **Sketcher constrain** toolbar, click the **Constrain point onto object** icon.

7. Select the endpoint of the external geometry and the horizontal line, as shown.

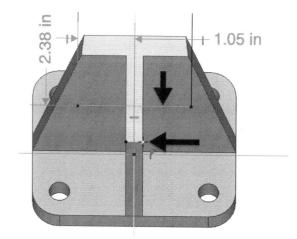

8. Click **Close** on the **Combo View** panel.
9. On the **Part Design Modelling** toolbar, click the **Pad** icon.
10. Type **0.31** in the **Length** box of the **Pad Parameters** dialog.
11. Click **OK**.

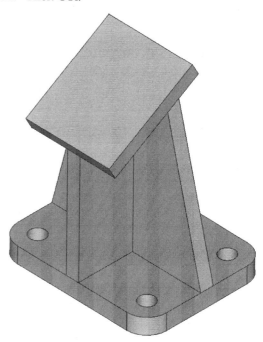

12. Add fillets of 0.31 in radius, as shown.

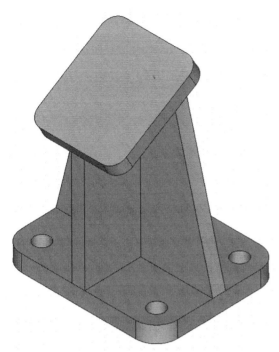

13. Click on the inclined face, as shown.

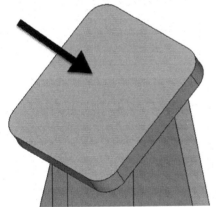

14. On the **Part Design Helper** toolbar, click the **Create Sketch** icon.

15. Click the **External geometry** icon on the **Sketcher geometries** toolbar.

16. Select the curved edges of the model, as shown.

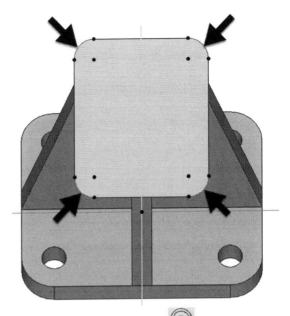

17. Click the **Create Circle** on the **Sketcher geometries** toolbar.

18. Create circles, as shown.

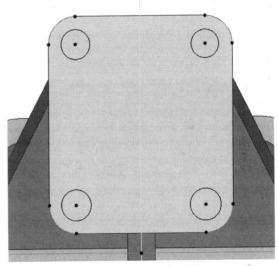

19. Click **Close** on the **Combo View** panel.
20. Click the **Hole** icon on the **Part Design Modeling** toolbar.
21. Type **0.31** in the **Diameter** box.
22. Select **Depth > Dimension**.
23. Type **0.31** in the **Depth** box.
24. Click **OK** on the **Combo View** panel; the holes are created.

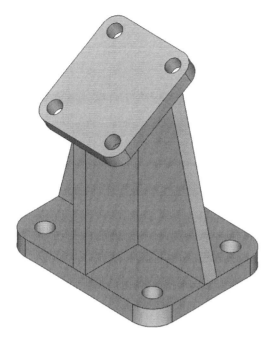

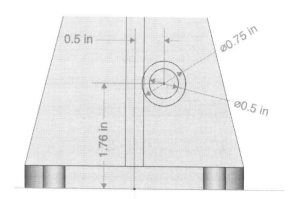

25. Click on the vertical face, as shown.

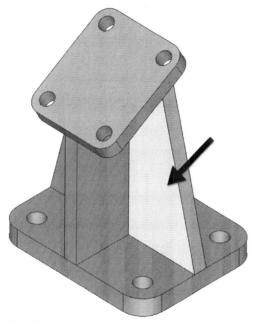

26. On the **Part Design Helper** toolbar, click the **Create Sketch** icon.
27. Create two circles and add dimensions to it, as shown.

28. Click **Close** on the **Combo View** panel.
29. On the **Part Design Modeling** toolbar, click the **Pad** icon.
30. Select **Type > Two dimensions**.
31. Type **0.59** in the **Length** box of the **Pad Parameters** dialog.
32. Type **0.79** in the **2nd Length** box and click **OK**.

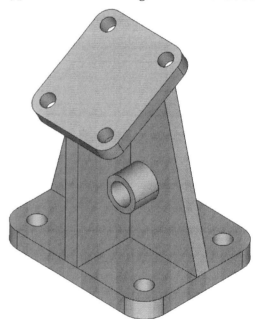

Creating the Pocket Feature

1. Click on the vertical face, as shown.

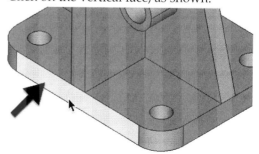

2. On the **Part Design Helper** toolbar, click the **Create Sketch** icon.
3. Create a rectangle and add dimensions to it.

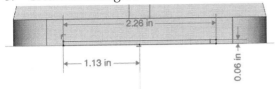

4. Click **Close** on the **Combo View** panel.
5. On the **Part Design Modeling** toolbar, click the **Pocket** icon.
6. Select **Type > Through all**.
7. Click **OK**.

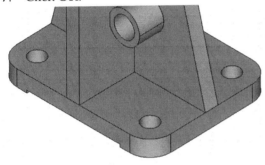

8. Save and close the file.

TUTORIAL 12

In this tutorial, you will create a spreadsheet and use the data in the spreadsheet to control the model.

1. Start a new file and select the **Part Design** option from the **Workbenches** drop-down.
2. Activate the Create **Sketch** command and select the XY plane. Next, click **OK**.
3. Create the sketch, as shown.

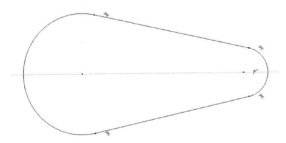

4. Click **Sketch > Sketcher Constraints > Constrain radius or weight** on the menu bar.
5. Select the large arc.
6. On the **Rapid Dimension** dialog, check the **Expression** on the **Driving** section.
7. Type **30** and press ENTER.
8. Select the small arc.

9. Type **15** and press ENTER.
10. Click the **Constrain horizontal distance** icon on the **Sketcher constraints** toolbar.
11. Select the sketch origin and the center point of the small arc.
12. Type **60** and press ENTER.

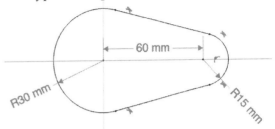

13. Click **Close** on the **Combo View** panel.
14. On the menu bar, click **Part Design > Create an additive feature > Pad**.
15. On the **Pad Parameters** section, type 15 in the **Length** box, and then click **OK**.

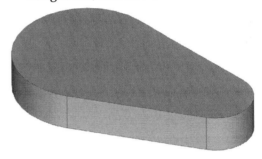

16. Press and hold the CTRL key and select the top and bottom faces of the model.
17. Click the **Thickness** icon on the **Part Design Modeling** toolbar.
18. Type **5** in the **Thickness** box
19. Check the **Make thickness inwards** option and click **OK**.

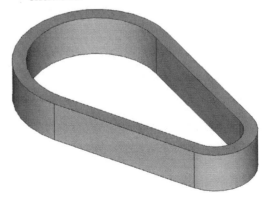

20. Select the **Spreadsheet** option from the **Workbenches** drop-down (or) click **View > Workbench > Spreadsheet** on the menu bar.

21. Click the **Create spreadsheet** 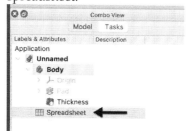 icon on the **Spreadsheet** toolbar (or) click the **Spreadsheet > Create Spreadsheet** on the menu bar.

22. Click the **Model** tab on the **Combo View** panel and double-click on the newly created spreadsheet.

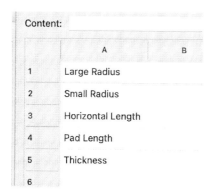

A spreadsheet is displayed in the window.

23. Double-click in the **A1** cell of the spreadsheet and type **Large Radius**.

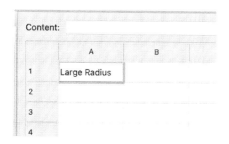

24. Likewise, enter **Small Radius**, **Horizontal Length**, **Pad Length**, and **Thickness** in the **A2**, **A3**, **A4**, and **A5** cells, respectively.

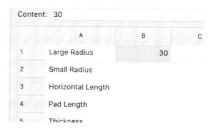

25. Double-click in the **B1** cell and type **30**.

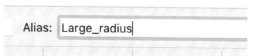

26. Click in the **Alias** box displayed at the top right corner of the spreadsheet and type **Large_radius**. Next, press ENTER.

Alias: Large_radius

27. Likewise, enter 15, 60, 15, and 5 in the B2, B3, B4, and B5 cells respectively.

Content:			
	A	B	C
1	Large Radius	30	
2	Small Radius	15	
3	Horizontal Length	60	
4	Pad Length	15	
5	Thickness	5	
6			

28. Enter **Small_radius**, **Horizontal_length**, **Pad_length**, and **Thickness** as the **Aliases** of **B2**, **B3**, **B4**, and **B5** cells respectively.

29. Click the **Model** tab on the **Combo View** panel and expand the **Pad** feature.

30. Right-click on the **Sketch**, and then select **Edit Sketch**.

31. Double-click on the 30 mm radius dimension.

32. Click the **Enter an expression** icon located in the **Radius** box on the **Insert Radius** dialog.

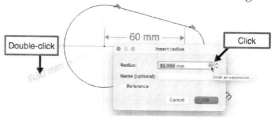

33. On the **Formula editor** dialog, type Spreadsheet, and then select the **Spreadsheet** option.

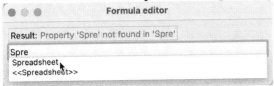

34. Click next to the Spreadsheet. value and type La. Next, select the **Large_radius** value from the listed value.

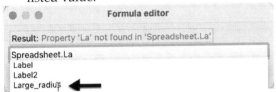

35. Click **OK** on the **Formula editor** dialog.

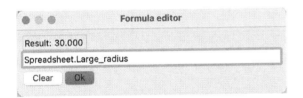

36. Click **OK** on the **Insert radius** dialog.
37. Double-click on the 15 mm radius value, and then click the **Enter an expression** button in the **Radius** box.

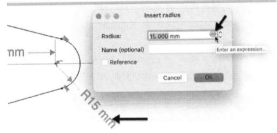

38. Type **Spreadsheet.Small_radius** in the **Formula editor** dialog. Next, click **OK** twice.

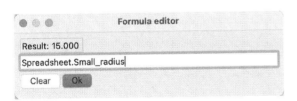

39. Likewise, change the 60 mm dimension value to **Spreadsheet.Horizontal_length** formula using the **Formula editor** dialog.

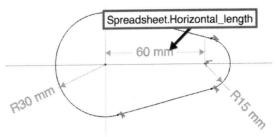

40. Click **Close** on the **Combo View** panel.
41. On the **Combo View** panel, right-click on the **Pad** feature, and then select **Edit Pad**.
42. Click the **Enter an expression** button in the **Length** box.

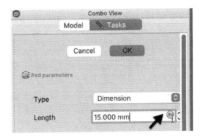

43. Type **Spreadsheet.Pad_length** in the **Formula editor** dialog. Next, click **OK**.

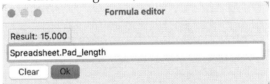

44. Click **OK** on the **Combo View** panel.
45. On the **Combo View** panel, right-click on the **Thickness** feature, and then select **Edit Thickness**.
46. Click the **Enter an expression** button in the **Thickness** box.
47. Type **Spreadsheet.Thickness** in the **Formula editor** dialog. Next, click **OK**.
48. Click **OK** on the **Combo View** panel.
49. Double-click on the Spreadsheet feature in the **Combo View** panel to open the spreadsheet.
50. Click in the B1 cell and change the value to 40.

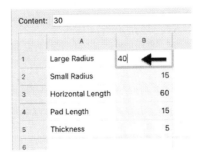

51. Switch to the model window and notice that the model is updated, as shown.

52. Likewise, change the other values in the spreadsheet and notice the updated model.

53. Save and close the part file.

TUTORIAL 13

In this tutorial, you will create expressions to drive the parameters of a bolt.

1. Start a new FreeCAD file and activate the Part Design workbench.
2. On the **Part Design Modeling** toolbar, click **Additive Primitives** drop-down > **Additive Cylinder**.

3. Select the YZ_Plane from the graphics window.

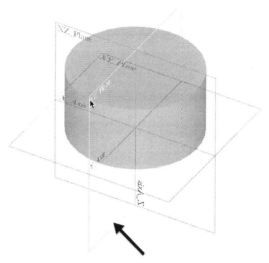

4. Type **10** and **80** in the **Radius** and **Height** boxes, respectively.

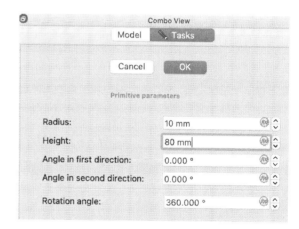

5. Click **OK** to create a cylinder.

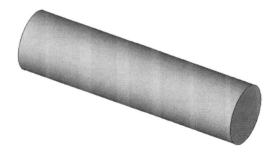

6. Select the right end face of the cylinder.
7. Click the **Create Sketch** icon on the **Part Design Helper** toolbar.

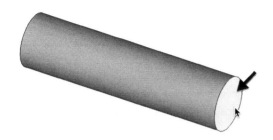

8. Create a hexagon, as shown.
9. Create a dimension between the sketch origin and the right vertex of the hexagon by selecting them.

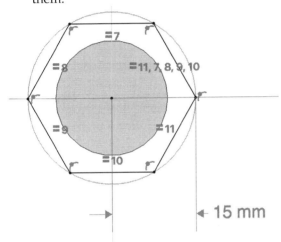

10. Click **Close** on the **Combo View** panel.
11. Click the **Pad** icon on the **Part Design Modeling** toolbar.
12. Type **10** in the **Length** box and click **OK**.

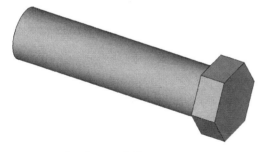

Creating the Spreadsheet
1. Select the **Spreadsheet** option from the **Workbenches** drop-down (or) click **View > Workbench > Spreadsheet** on the menu bar.

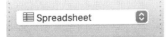

2. Click the **Create spreadsheet** icon on the **Spreadsheet** toolbar (or) click the **Spreadsheet > Create Spreadsheet** on the menu bar.
3. Click the **Model** tab on the **Combo View** panel

and double-click on the newly created spreadsheet.
4. Type-in the values in the **B** and **C** columns in the spreadsheet.
5. Specify the Aliases for the values in the **B** and **C** columns, as shown.

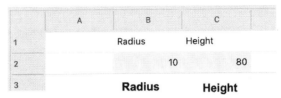

13. On the **Combo View** panel, click the **Cylinder** feature.
14. Click the **Data** tab at the bottom of the **Combo View** panel.
15. Scroll to the **Cylinder** section on the **Data** tab of the **Combo View** panel.
16. Click in the Radius box and click the Enter an expression icon.
17. Type **Spreadsheet.Radius** in the **Formula editor** dialog and click **OK**.

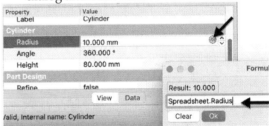

18. Likewise, change the **Height** value to **Spreadsheet.Height**.

Cylinder	
Radius	10.000 mm (Spreadsheet.Radius)
Angle	360.000 °
Height	80.000 mm (Spreadsheet.Height)

19. Click the **Model** tab on the **Combo View** panel and expand the **Pad** feature.
20. Right-click on the **Sketch**, and then select **Edit Sketch**.
21. Double-click on the 15 mm dimension.
22. Click the **Enter an expression** icon located in the **Length** box on the **Insert Radius** dialog.
23. On the **Formula editor** dialog, type 2*Spreadsheet.Radius, and then click **OK**.

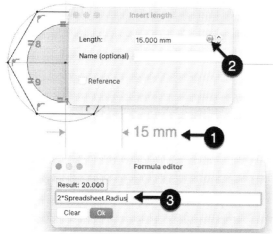

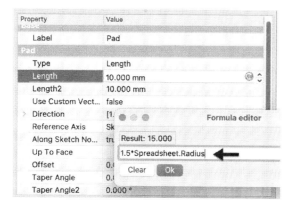

24. On the **Combo View** panel, click the **Pad** feature.
25. Click the **Data** tab at the bottom of the **Combo View** panel.
26. Scroll to the **Pad** section on the **Data** tab of the **Combo View** panel.
27. Click in the **Length** box.
28. Click the **Enter an expression**.
29. Type **1.5*Spreadsheet.Radius** in the **Formula editor** dialog.
30. Click **OK**.

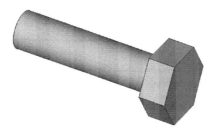

31. Switch to the model window and notice that the model is updated.

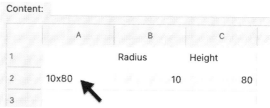

Creating Configuration Table

1. Double-click on the **Spreadsheet** in the **Combo View** panel.

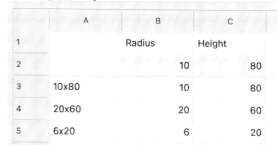

2. Enter **10x80**, **20x60** and **6x20** in the **A3**, **A4**, and **A5** cells.
3. Enter **10**, **20** and **6** in the **B3**, **B4,** and **B5** cells, respectively.
4. Enter **80**, **60** and **20** in the **C3**, **C4**, and **C5** cells, respectively.

	A	B	C
1		Radius	Height
2		10	80
3	10x80	10	80
4	20x60	20	60
5	6x20	6	20

5. Click the right-mouse button in the **A2** cell and select **Configuration Table** from the shortcut menu.

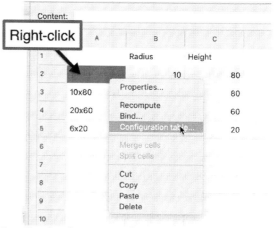

6. On the **Setup Configuration Table** dialog, type **Configuration** (or any name) in the **Property** box.
7. Type **Parameters** (or any name) in the **Group** box and click **OK**.

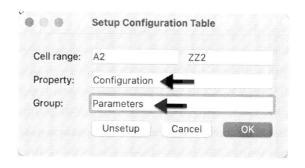

131

8. On the menu bar, click **Windows > Tile**.

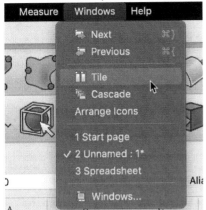

9. Click on the **Spreadsheet** in the **Combo View** panel.
10. Click the **Data** tab at the bottom of the **Combo View** panel.
11. Select **Configurations > 20x60**.

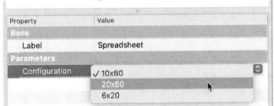

12. Click in the spreadsheet and notice that the model is updated, as shown.

13. Select **Configuration > 6x20** and click in the spreadsheet. The model is updated, as shown.

14. Add one more configuration to the table, as shown.

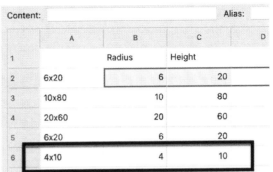

Content:		Alias:	
	A	B	C	D
1		Radius	Height	
2	6x20	6	20	
3	10x80	10	80	
4	20x60	20	60	
5	6x20	6	20	
6	4x10	4	10	

15. Select **Configuration > 4x10** and click in the spreadsheet.

16. Save and close the part file.

Chapter 6: Creating Drawings

In this chapter, you generate 2D drawings of the parts. You learn to:

- Insert standard views of a part model
- Add dimensions

TUTORIAL 1

In this tutorial, you create the drawing of the Tutorial 7 file created in the fourth chapter.

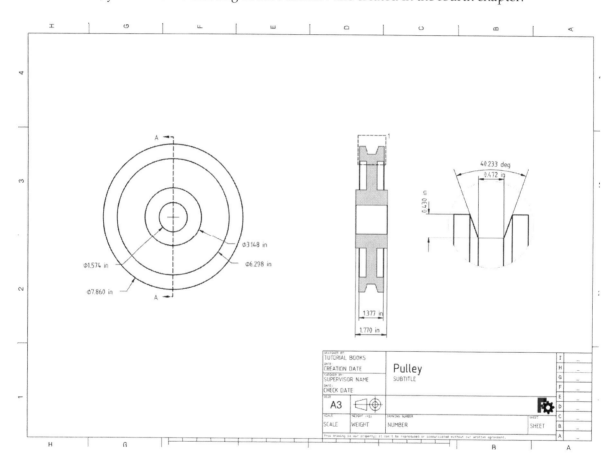

Starting a New Drawing File

1. Click **File > Open** on the Menu bar.
2. Go to the location of the Tutorial 7 file of Chapter 5.
3. Select the Tutorial 7 file and click the **Open** button.
4. Click **Edit > Preferences** on the Menu bar.

The **Preferences** dialog box appears. If you are working on MacOS, then click **FreeCAD > Preferences** on the title bar.

5. On the **Preferences** dialog box, click the **TechDraw** option at the left side and then click the **Dimensions** tab.
6. Select **Standard ans Style > ASME Inlined**.

7. Click **OK**.
8. Select **TechDraw** from the **Workbenches** drop-down.
9. Click the **Insert new drawing page from template** 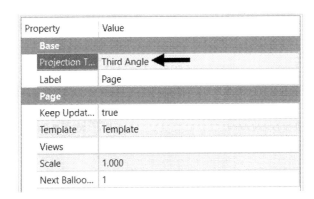 icon on the **TechDraw Pages** toolbar.
10. Select the **A3_LandscapeTD** template.
11. Click **Open**.
12. In the **Combo View** panel, select the **Page** from the **Model** tab.
13. Click the **Data** tab on the bottom of the **Combo View** panel.
14. In the **Properties** section of the **Combo View** panel, select **Projection Type > Third Angle**.

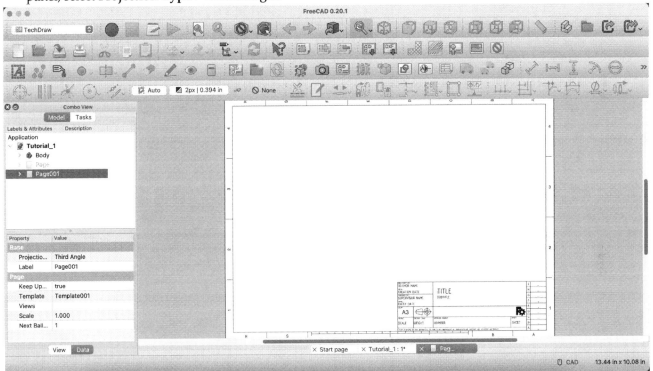

Generating the Base View

1. Click the **Tutorial 7** tab on the bottom of the window.

2. Select the front face of the model.

3. Click the **Page** tab on the bottom of the window.

4. To generate the base view, click the **Insert Projection Group** icon on the **TechDraw Views** toolbar.

5. On the **Projection Group** section, select **Scale > Custom**.

6. Type **1** and **2** in the **Scale Numerator** and **Scale Denominator** boxes located next to **Custom Scale**.

7. Click **OK** on the **Combo View** panel.

8. Click on the dotted borderline of the view.

9. Press and hold the left mouse and drag the view to left.

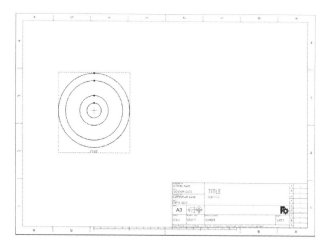

Generating the Section View

1. Select the base view.

2. Click the **Insert section view in drawing** icon on the **TechDraw Views** toolbar.

3. Click the **Looking left** icon on the **Quick Section Parameters** section.

4. Type **0** in the **X**, **Y**, and **Z** boxes, respectively. These values define the location of the section plane.

5. Type **A** in the **Identifier** box.

6. Click **OK** to create the section view.

7. Select the section view from the drawing page.

8. Click the **Position Section View** icon on the **TechDraw Attributes** toolbar. The section view is horizontally in-line with the base view.

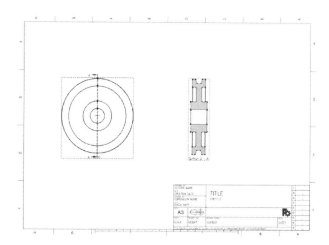

Creating the Detailed View

Now, you have to create the detailed view of the groove, which is displayed, in the section view.

1. Select the section view.

2. Click the **Insert detail view in drawing** icon on the **TechDraw Views** toolbar.

3. In the **New Detail View** section, type **20** mm in the **Radius** box.

4. Type **1.5** in the **Scale** box. The detailed view is generated.

5. Drag the detailed view to the right side on the drawing sheet.

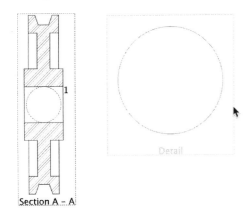

Now, you need to specify the portion of the section view to be displayed in the detailed view.

6. Click the **Drag Highlight** button on the **Combo View** panel.

7. Click on the drag text displayed next to the boundary of the detail view.

8. Drag it upward and place at the location, as shown.

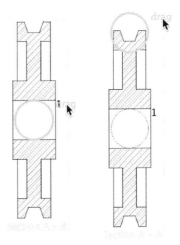

9. Click **OK**.

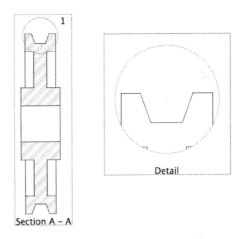

Adding Dimensions

Now, you add dimensions to the drawing.

1. Select the outer circular edge of the base view.

2. Click the **Diameter dimension** icon on the **TechDraw Dimensions** toolbar.

3. Click and drag the dimension outside the view.

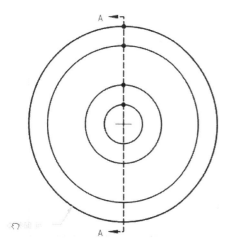

4. Likewise, add remaining dimensions to the base view, as shown.

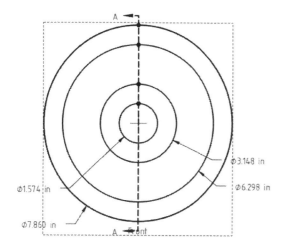

5. Press and hold the Ctrl key and select the vertical edges of the section view, as shown.

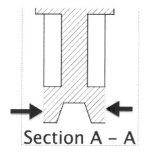

6. Click the **Horizontal-distance dimension** icon on the **TechDraw Dimensions** toolbar.

7. Click in the drawing page to deselect the selected edges.

8. Press and hold the Ctrl key and select the vertical edges of the section view, as shown.

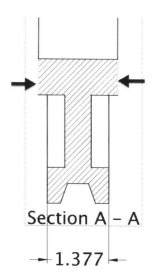

9. Click the **Horizontal-distance dimension** icon on the **TechDraw Dimensions** toolbar.

10. Press and hold the CTRL key and select the two newly created dimensions.

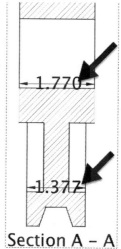

11. On the **TechDraw Attributes** toolbar, click the **Cascade dimensions** drop-down > **Cascade Horizontal Dimensions**. The selected dimensions are arranged.

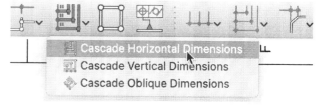

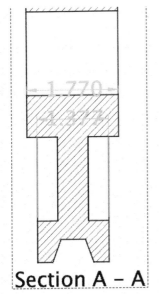

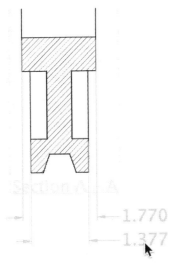

12. Drag the dimension values downward, and then toward right, as shown.

13. Click in the drawing page to deselect the selected dimensions.

14. Press and hold the Ctrl key and select the two inclined lines in the detailed view, as shown.

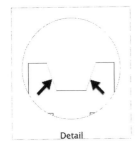

15. Click the **Angle Dimension** icon on the **TechDraw Dimensions** toolbar.

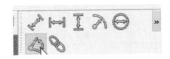

16. Press and hold the Ctrl key and select the horizontal edges of the detailed view, as shown.

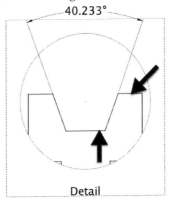

17. Click the **Vertical-distance dimension** icon on the **TechDraw Dimensions** toolbar.

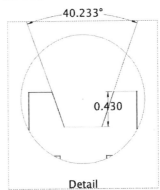

18. Create the remaining dimension, as shown.

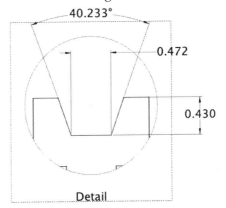

138

Populating the Title Block

1. Zoom in to the title block area.
2. Double-click on the green square displayed on TITLE.

3. Type **Pulley** in the **Value** box.
4. Click **OK**.

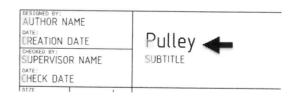

5. Likewise, add data to the remaining fields in the Title block.
6. Save and close the file.

Chapter 7: Sheet Metal Modeling

TUTORIAL 1

In this tutorial, you create the sheet metal model shown in the figure.

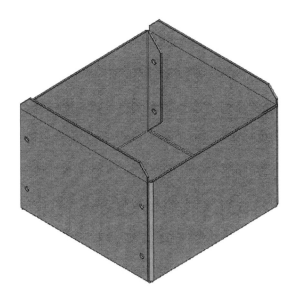

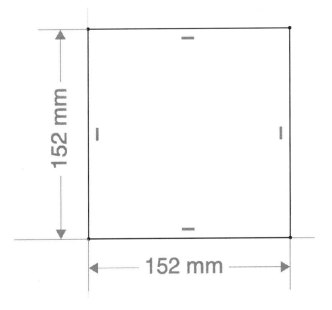

Creating the Base Feature

1. Open a new FreeCAD file.
2. Click **Tools > Addon Manager** on the Menu bar.
3. On the **Addon Manager** dialog, click the **Workbenches** tab.
4. Select **Sheetmetal Workbench** from the list.
5. Click **Install**.
6. Click **Close** twice.
7. Close the FreeCAD application, and then restart it.
8. Select **Sketcher** from the **Workbenches** drop-down.
9. Click the **Create Sketch** icon on the **Part Design Helper** toolbar.
10. Select the XY plane and click **OK**.
11. Click the **Create Polyline** icon on the **Sketcher geometries** toolbar.
12. Create a closed sketch, as shown.

13. Click the **Close** button on the **Combo View** panel.
14. Select **Sheet Metal** from the **Workbenches** drop-down.
15. Select the sketch, if not already selected.
16. Click the **Make Base Wall** icon on the **Sheetmetal** toolbar.
17. Select the **BaseBend** feature from the **Combo View** panel.

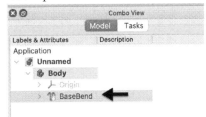

18. Click the **Data** tab at the bottom of the **Combo View** panel.
19. Type **1.5** in the **thickness** box.

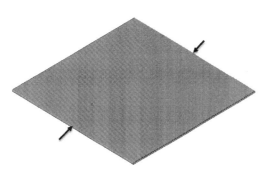

Creating the flange

1. Press and hold the CTRL key and select the edges on the top face, as shown.

2. Click the **Bend** icon on the **Sheetmetal** toolbar.
3. Click the **Model** tab on the **Combo View** panel.
4. Select **Bend** from the model tree.

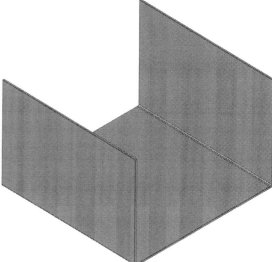

5. On the **Properties** panel, enter **100** and **1** in the

length and **radius** boxes, respectively.

6. Select **Bend Type > Offset**.
7. Enter **1.75** in the **offset** box.
8. Select **invert > true**.

9. Press and hold the CTRL key and select the edges on the top face, as shown.

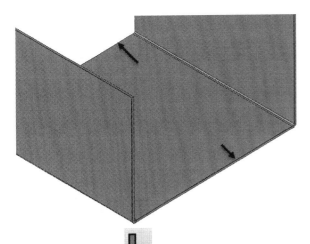

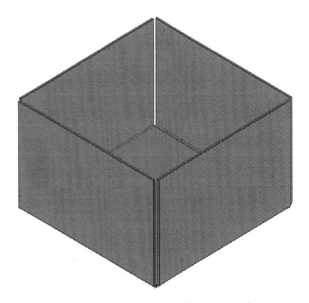

10. Click the **Bend** 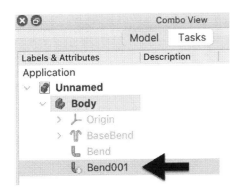 icon on the **Sheetmetal** toolbar.
11. Select **Bend001** from the **Model** tab of the **Combo View** panel.

15. Select the inner edge of the flange, as shown.

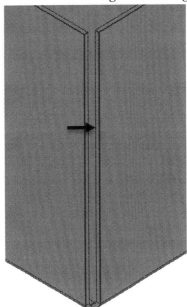

12. Select **Bend Type > Material Outside**.
13. Select **invert > true**.
14. Type **100** in the **length** box.

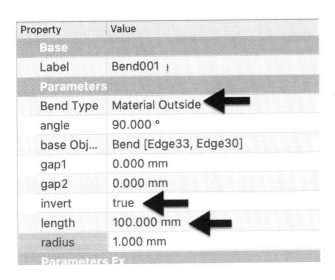

16. Click the **Bend** icon on the **Sheetmetal** toolbar.
17. Select **Bend002** from the **Model** tab of the **Combo View** panel.
18. Select **Bend Type > Material Outside**.
19. Type **15** in the **length** box.
20. Select **invert > true**.
21. In the **Parameters Ex** section, select **Auto Miter > false**.
22. Type **45** in the **miterangle1** and **miterangle2** boxes, respectively.

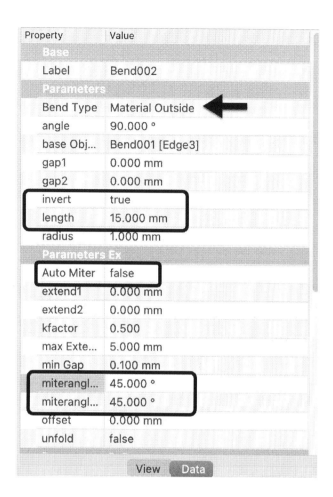

Property	Value
Base	
Label	Bend002
Parameters	
Bend Type	Material Outside
angle	90.000 °
base Obj...	Bend001 [Edge3]
gap1	0.000 mm
gap2	0.000 mm
invert	true
length	15.000 mm
radius	1.000 mm
Parameters Ex	
Auto Miter	false
extend1	0.000 mm
extend2	0.000 mm
kfactor	0.500
max Exte...	5.000 mm
min Gap	0.100 mm
miterangl...	45.000 °
miterangl...	45.000 °
offset	0.000 mm
unfold	false

View   Data

23. Press and hold the middle mouse button and the right mouse button.
24. Drag the pointer toward left such that the other end of the flange is displayed.

The flange is displayed.

25. Likewise, create three more miter flanges, as shown.

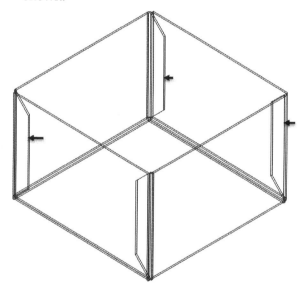

Extending a face

1. Press and hold the CTRL key and select the outer edges of the flanges, as shown.

143

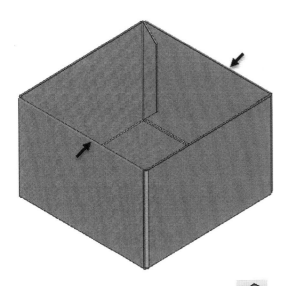

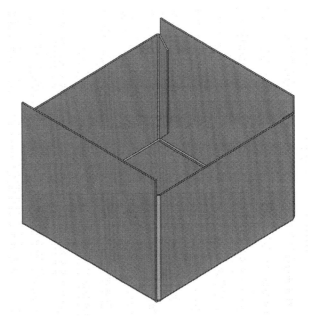

2. Click the **Extend a face along normal** 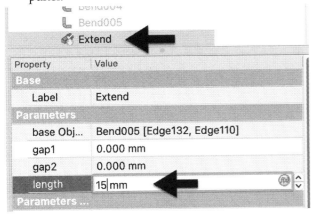 icon on the **My Commands** toolbar.

3. Select **Extend** from the **Model** tab of the **Combo View** panel.

4. Type **15** in the **Length** box of the **Properties** panel.

5. Select **Part Design** from the **Workbenches** drop-down.

6. Select the edge of the extended face, as shown.

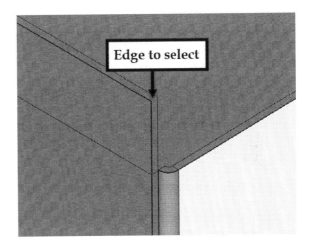

7. On the **Part Design Modeling** toolbar, click the **Chamfer** icon.

8. On the **Chamfer parameters** dialog, click the **Add** button.

9. Select the corner edge of the extended face, as shown.

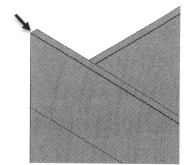

10. Likewise, use the **Add** button and select the corner edges of another extended face.

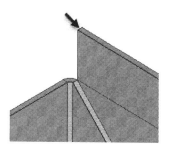

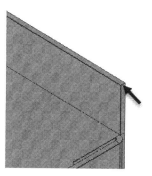

11. Type **10** in the **Size** box and click **OK**.

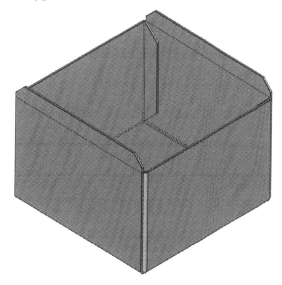

Creating the Pockets

1. Select the flat face of the flange.

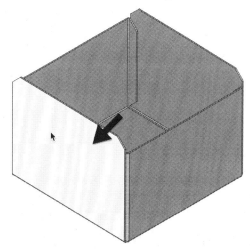

2. Click the **Create Sketch** icon on the **Part Design Helper** toolbar.

3. On the **View** toolbar, click **Draw Style** drop-down > **Wireframe**.

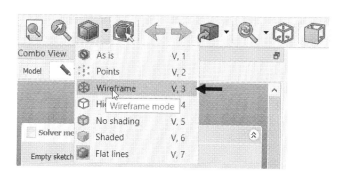

4. Create four circles, as shown.

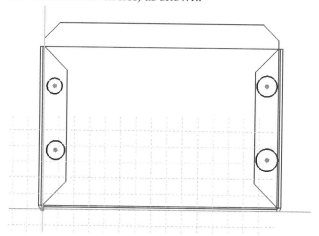

5. Click the **Constrain equal** icon on the **Sketcher constraints** toolbar.

6. Select all the circles one-by-one in the clockwise direction.
7. Select the first and last circle; all the circles are made equal in diameter.
8. Press ESC.
9. Select the center points of the two circles, as shown.
10. Click the **Constrain horizontally** ▬ icon on the **Sketcher constraints** toolbar.
11. Select the center points of the remaining two circles.
12. Click the **Constrain horizontally** ▬ icon on the **Sketcher constraints** toolbar.

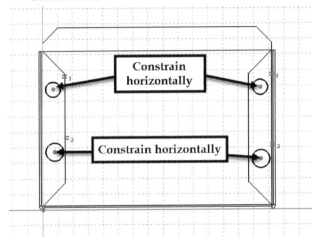

13. Select the centerpoints of the two circles, as shown.
14. Click the **Constrain vertically** ▌ icon on the **Sketcher constraints** toolbar.
15. Select the centerpoints of the two circles, as shown.
16. Click the **Constrain vertically** ▌ icon on the **Sketcher constraints** toolbar.

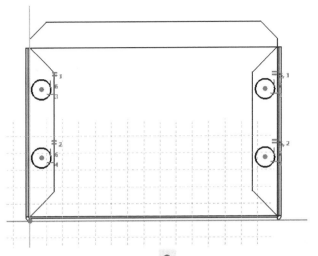

17. Click the **Create point** ● icon on the **Sketcher geometries** toolbar.
18. Click in the center of the model.
19. Add vertical and horizontal dimensions to the point, as shown.

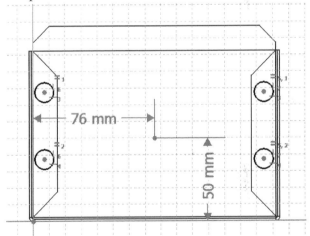

20. Click the **Constrain symmetrical** ✂ icon on the **Sketcher constraints** toolbar.
21. Select the center point of the top-right circle.
22. Select the center point of the bottom-left circle.
23. Select the newly created point.

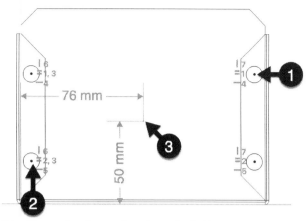

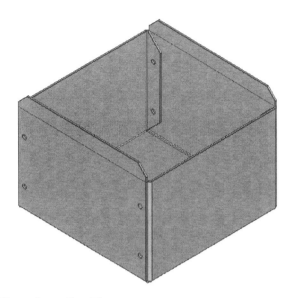

24. Create horizontal and vertical distance constraints, as shown.
25. Create the diameter constraint, as shown.

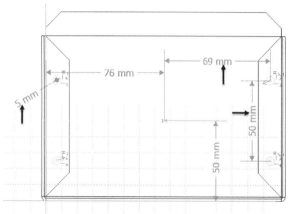

26. Click **Leave Sketch** on **the Sketcher** toolbar.
27. On the **Part Design Modeling** toolbar, click the **Pocket** icon.
28. On the **Pocket Parameters** dialog, select **Type > Through All**.
29. Click **OK**.
30. On the **View** toolbar, click **Draw Style** drop-down > **Flat Lines**.

Creating the Flat Pattern

1. Select **Sheet Metal** from the **Workbenches** drop-down.
2. Click on the flat face of the sheet metal model.

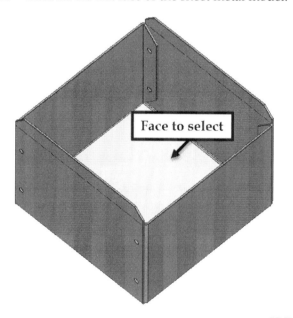

3. Click the **Flatten folder sheet metal object** icon on the **Sheetmetal** toolbar.
4. Keep the **Manual K-factor** option checked on the **Unfold sheet metal object** dialog.
5. Select the **ANSI** option.
6. Click **OK**.

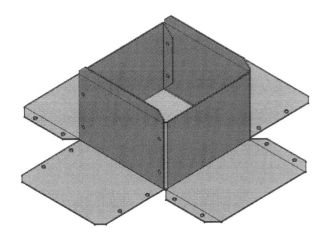

7. Save the sheet metal part.

Creating 2D Drawing of the sheet metal part

1. Select **TechDraw** from the **Workbenches** dropdown.

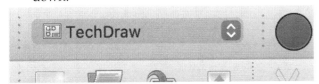

2. Click the **Insert new Page using Template** icon on the **TechDraw pages** toolbar.

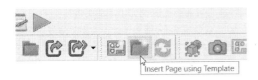

3. Double-click on the **A2_Landscape_ISO7200TD** template.
4. Select **Body** from the **Model** tab.

5. Click the **Insert Projection Group** icon on the **Techdraw Views** toolbar.

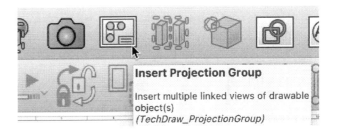

Insert Projection Group
Insert multiple linked views of drawable object(s)
(TechDraw_ProjectionGroup)

6. On the **Projection Group** dialog, select **Scale > Custom**.
7. Type **1** and **2** in the **Custom Scale** boxes, respectively.

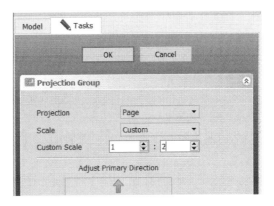

8. Click **OK** on the **Projection Group** dialog.
9. Click the **Refresh** icon on the **File** toolbar.
10. Switch to the drawing sheet tab.
11. Click and drag the view to the bottom right corner, as shown.

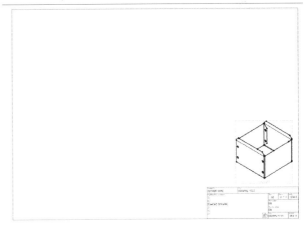

12. Switch to the sheet metal model file.
13. On the **View** toolbar, click the **Set to top view** icon.

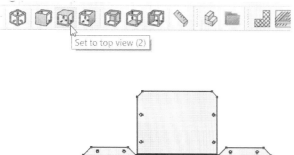

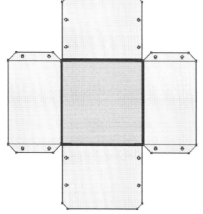

14. Switch to the drawing view.
15. Select **Unfold_Sketch** from the **Model** tab.

16. Click the **Insert Projection Group** icon on the **Techdraw Views** toolbar.
17. On the **Projection Group** dialog, select **Scale > Custom**.
18. Type **3** and **4** in the **Custom Scale** boxes, respectively.
19. Click **OK** on the **Projection Group** dialog.

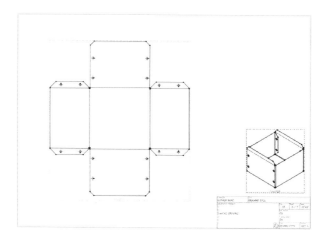

20. Add dimensions to the unfolded view.

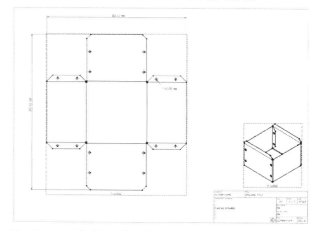

21. Save and close the sheet metal files.

TUTORIAL 2

In this tutorial, you create the model shown in the figure.

Creating the Base Feature

20. Open a new FreeCAD file.
21. Select **Part Design** from the **Workbenches** drop-down.
22. Click the **Create Sketch** icon on the **Part Design Helper** toolbar.

23. Select the XY plane and click **OK**.
24. Click the **Rectangle** drop-down > **Centered Rectangle** on the **Sketcher geometries** toolbar.
25. Create a rectangle and add dimensions to it, as shown.

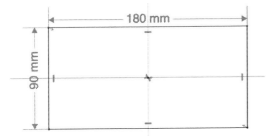

26. Click the **Close** button on the **Combo View** panel.
27. Click **Part Design > Create an additive feature > Pad** on the menu bar.
28. Type **15** in the **Length** box and click **OK**.

29. Press and hold the middle and right mouse buttons. Next, drag the pointer to rotate the model.
30. Click on the bottom face of the model.
31. Click **Create Sketch** on the **Part Design Helper** toolbar.
32. On the menu bar, click **Sketch > Sketcher geometries > Toggle construction geometry**.
33. Click **Rectangle** drop-down > **Centered rectangle** on the **Sketcher geometries** toolbar.
34. Select the sketch origin, move the pointer outward and click.
35. Click the **Toggle construction geometry** icon on the **Sketcher geometries** toolbar.
36. Create four circles on the vertices of the rectangle.
37. Add constraints and dimensions to the sketch.
38. Click **Close** on the **Combo View** panel.

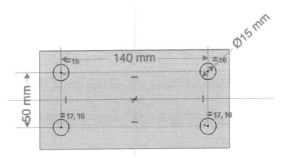

39. Click the **Pad** icon on the **Part Design Modeling** toolbar.
40. Type **8** in the **Length** box and click **OK**.
41. Press and hold the CTRL key and click on the bottom faces of the second Pad feature.

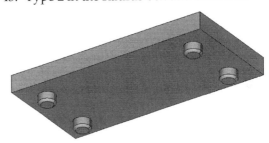

42. Click the **Fillet** icon on the **Part Design Modeling** toolbar.
43. Type 2 in the **Radius** box and click **OK**.

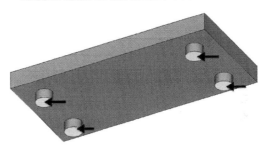

44. Click on the bottom face of the first Pad feature.
45. Click the **Create Sketch** icon on the **Part Design Helper** toolbar.
46. Create a centered rectangle and add dimensions to it, as shown.

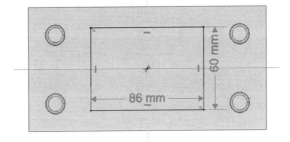

47. Click the **Close** button on the **Combo View**

panel.

48. Click **Part Design > Create an additive feature > Pad** on the menu bar.
49. Type **25** in the **Length** box and click **OK**.

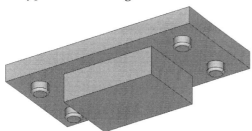

50. Press and hold the CTRL key and select the vertical edges of the newly created Pad feature.
51. Click the **Fillet** icon on the **Part Design Modeling** toolbar.
52. Type **10** in the **Radius** box and click **OK**.

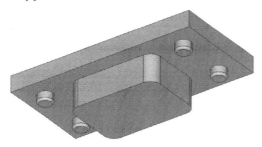

53. Click on the bottom face of the newly created Pad feature.

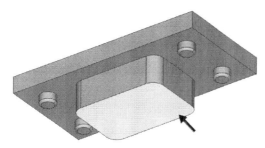

54. Type **2** in the **Radius** box and click **OK**.
55. Click on the edge of the model, as shown.

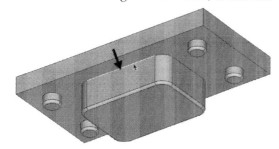

56. Click the **Fillet** icon on the **Part Design Modeling** toolbar.

57. Type **5** in the **Radius** box and click **OK**.

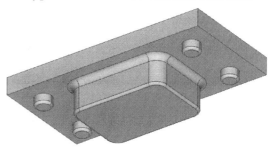

58. Press and hold the CTRL key and click on the vertical edges of the model, as shown.

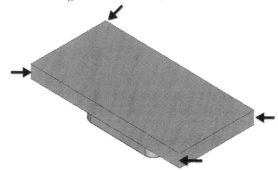

59. Click the **Thickness** icon on the **Part Design Modeling** toolbar.
60. Type **18** in the **Radius** box and click **OK**.

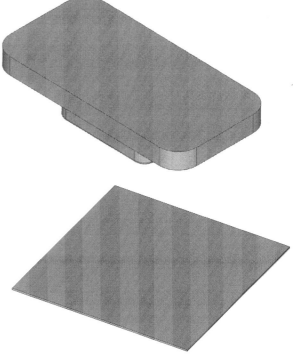

Creating Thickness feature

26. Press and hold the CTRL key and select top face

and the side faces attached to it, as shown.

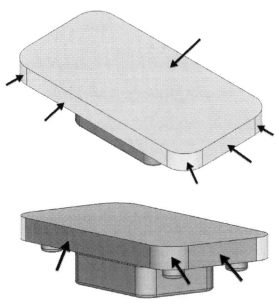

27. Click the **Add face** button on the **Combo View** panel.
28. Rotate the model and select the bottom faces of the Pad features.

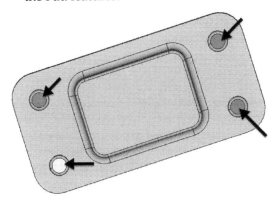

29. Type **1** in the **Thickness** box.
30. Click **OK**.

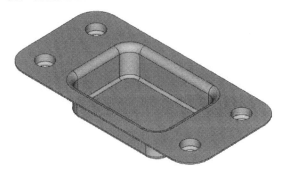

31. Save and close the file.

TUTORIAL 3

In this tutorial, you create the sheet metal model shown in the figure.

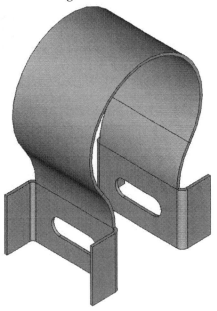

Creating the Base Feature

1. Open a new FreeCAD file.
2. Select **Sketcher** from the **Workbenches** drop-down.
3. Click the **Create Sketch** icon on the **Sketcher** toolbar.
4. Select the **YZ-Plane** option and click **OK**.
5. Select the **Arc** drop-down > **Center and end points** from the **Sketcher geometries** toolbar.
6. Select the sketch origin to define the center of the arc.
7. Specify the start and end points of the arc, as shown.

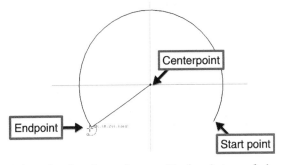

8. Select the **Arc** drop-down > **End points and rim points** from the **Sketcher geometries** toolbar.
9. Select the endpoint of the arc.
10. Move the pointer downward and click.

11. Move the pointer toward right and click to create the arc.

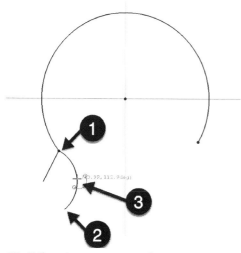

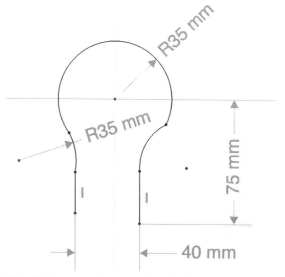

12. Likewise, create another arc, as shown.

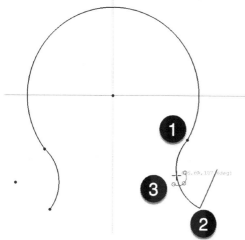

15. Add constraints to the sketch, as shown.

13. Create two vertical lines from the endpoints of the arcs, as shown.

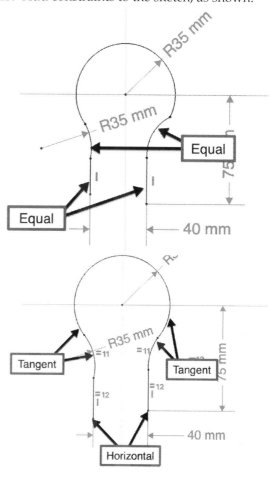

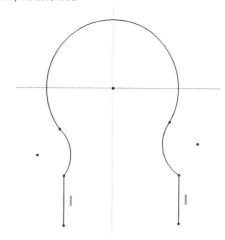

14. Add dimensions to the sketch, as shown.

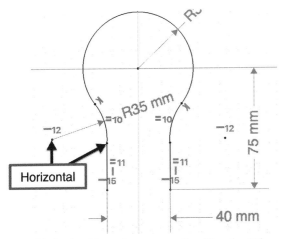

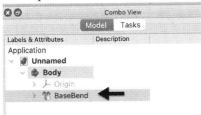

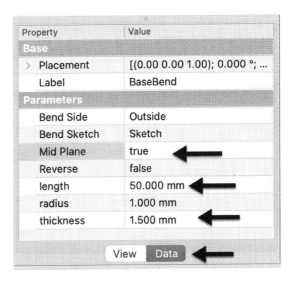

16. Click the **Close** button on the **Combo View** panel.
17. Select **Sheet Metal** from the **Workbenches** drop-down.
18. Select the sketch, if not already selected.
19. Click the **Make Base Wall** icon on the **Sheetmetal** toolbar.
20. Select the **BaseBend** feature from the **Combo View** panel.

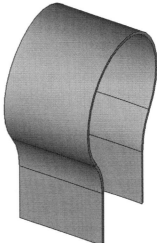

21. Click the **Data** tab at the bottom of the **Combo View** panel.
22. Type **1.5** in the **thickness** box.
23. Type **50** in the **length** box.
24. Select **Mid Plane > true**.

Creating the flange

1. Press and hold the CTRL key and select the edges, as shown.

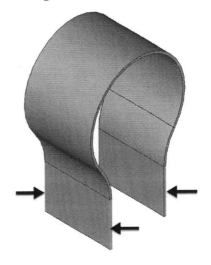

2. Click the **Bend** icon on the **Sheetmetal** toolbar.
3. Click the **Model** tab on the **Combo View** panel.
4. Select **Bend** from the model tree.

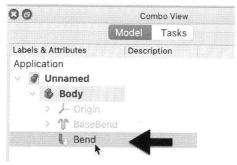

5. On the **Properties** panel, select **invert > true**.
6. Enter **18** and **2** in the **length** and **radius** boxes, respectively.
7. Select **Length Spec > Outer Sharp**.
8. Select **Bend Type > Material Outside**.
9. Select **invert > true**.

Property	Value
Label	Bend
Parameters	
Bend Type	Material Outside
Length Spec	Outer Sharp
angle	90.000 °
base Object	BaseBend [Edge14, Edge...
gap1	0.000 mm
gap2	0.000 mm
invert	true
length	18.000 mm
radius	2.000 mm

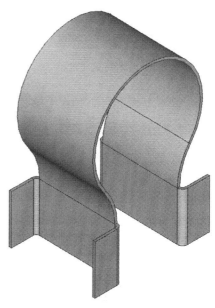

Creating Extruded Cuts

12. Select **Sketcher** from the **Workbenches** drop-down.
13. Click on the flat face of the flange, as shown.

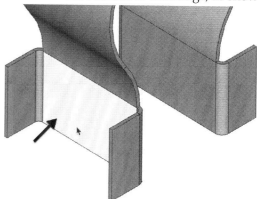

14. Click the **Create Sketch** icon on the **Sketcher** toolbar.
15. Select the **Flatface** option and click **OK**.

16. Select the **Create slot** icon from the **Sketcher geometries** toolbar.
17. Create a slot and add dimensions to it, as shown.

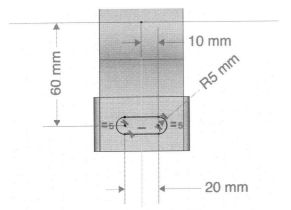

18. Click **Close** on the **Combo View** panel.
19. Select **Sheetmetal** from the **Workbenches** drop-down.
20. Select the flat face of the sheet metal model, as shown.

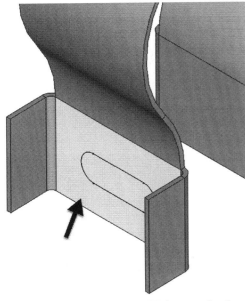

21. Press and hold the CTRL key and select the newly created sketch from the **Combo View** panel.

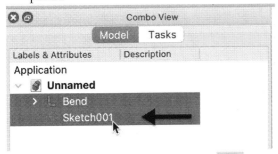

22. Click the **Sketch on Sheet Metal** icon on the **Sheetmetal** toolbar. An extruded cut is created on the flat face using the sketch.

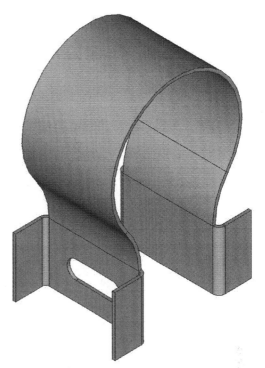

23. Likewise, create another extruded cut on the right vertical face of the sheet metal body.

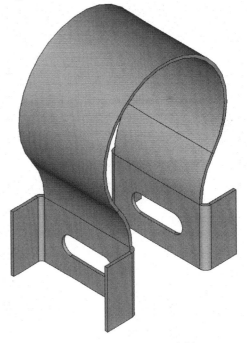

24. Save and close the sheet metal file.

TUTORIAL 4

In this tutorial, you create the sheet metal model shown in the figure.

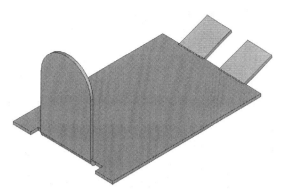

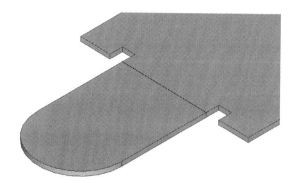

Adding Corner Reliefs

1. Download the Ch7-tutorial3 file by sending us email to freecadtuts@gmail.com
2. Open the downloaded file.
3. Select **Sheet Metal** from the **Workbenches** dropdown.
4. Click on the lower endpoint of the vertical edge, as shown.

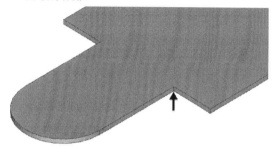

5. Press and hold the CTRL key and select the upper endpoint of the vertical edge, as shown.

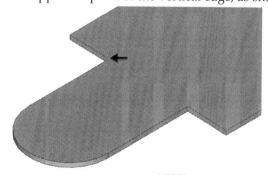

6. Click the **Make Relief** ⬜ icon on the **Sheet Metal** toolbar. Reliefs are added at the selected corners.

7. Select the **Relief** feature from the **Combo View** panel.
8. Click the **Data** tab on the **Combo View** panel.
9. Type **3** in the **relief** box.

Property	Value
Base	
Label	Relief
Parameters	
base Obj...	BaseBend [Vertex21, Vertex16]
relief	3.000 mm

| View | Data |

10. Click in the graphics window to update the relief size.

Fold a wall using a Sketch

1. Select **Part Design** from the **Workbenches** dropdown.
2. Click on the top face of the sheet metal part.
3. Click the **Create Sketch** icon on the **Part Design Helper** toolbar.
4. Click the **External geometry** icon on the **Sketcher geometries** toolbar.
5. Select the horizontal edges of the sheet metal part, as shown.

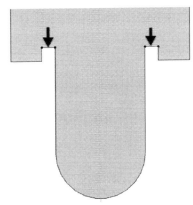

6. Click the **Create Line** icon on the **Sketcher geometries** toolbar.
7. Select the inner endpoint of the external geometry, as shown.

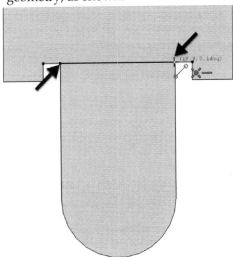

8. Click the **Close** button on the **Combo View** panel.
9. Click on the top face of the sheet metal part.
10. Click the **Create Sketch** icon on the **Part Design Helper** toolbar.
11. Click the **External geometry** icon on the **Sketcher geometries** toolbar.
12. Select the horizontal edges of the sheet metal part, as shown.

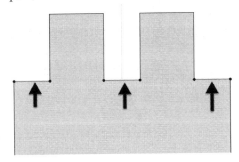

13. Click the **Create Line** icon on the **Sketcher geometries** toolbar.
14. Select the endpoints of the external geometry, as shown.

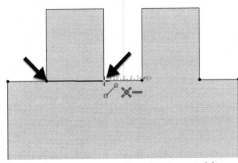

15. Likewise, create another horizontal line, as shown.

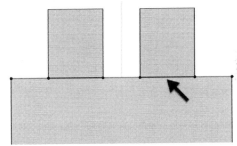

16. Select **Sheet Metal** from the **Workbenches** drop-down.
17. Press and hold the CTRL key and select the top face of the sheetmetal part and the line, as shown.

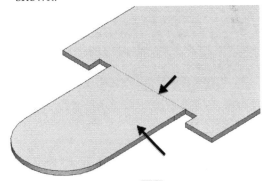

18. Click the **Fold a Wall** icon on the **Sheet Metal** toolbar. The wall is folded, as shown.

19. Press and hold the CTRL key and select the top face of the sheetmetal part and the lines, as shown.

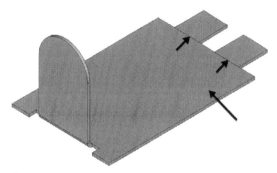

The wall is folded, as shown.

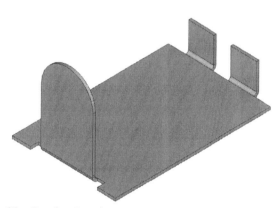

20. On the **Combo View** panel, click the Model tab and select the Fold001 feature.
21. Click the **Data** tab on the bottom of the **Combo View** panel.
22. Select **Position > Middle**. The position of the fold is changed to middle.

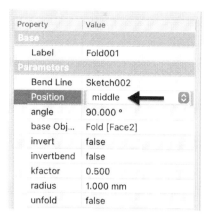

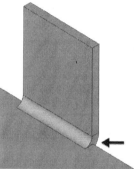

23. Select the **Position > Backward** to change the fold position to backward.

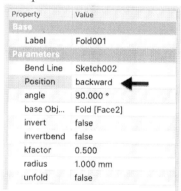

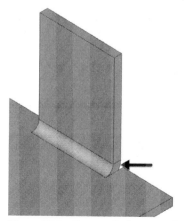

24. Type **20** in the **angle** box, and then click in the graphics window.

Property	Value
Base	
Label	Fold001
Parameters	
Bend Line	Sketch002
Position	backward
angle	20.000 °
base Obj...	Fold [Face2]
invert	false
invertbend	false
kfactor	0.500
radius	1.000 mm
unfold	false

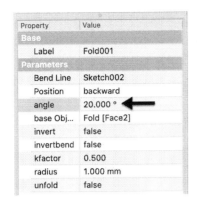

25. Save and close the file.

TUTORIAL 5

In this tutorial, you create the sheet metal model shown in the figure.

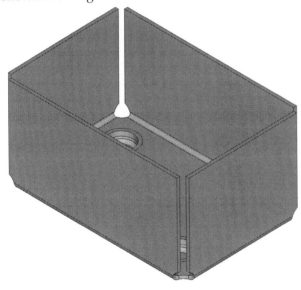

Ripping the Edges of the Model

1. Open a new FreeCAD file.
2. Close the FreeCAD application, and then restart it.
3. Select **Part Design** from the **Workbenches** drop-down.

4. Click the **Create Sketch** icon on the **Part Design Helper** toolbar.
5. Select the XY plane and click **OK**.
6. Click the **Rectangle** drop-down > **Centered Rectangle** on the **Sketcher geometries** toolbar.
7. Create a closed sketch, as shown.

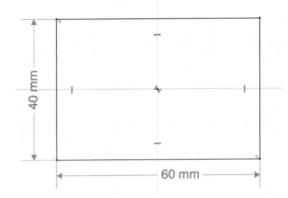

8. Click the **Close** button on the **Combo View** panel.
9. Click the **Pad** icon on the **Part Design Modeling** toolbar.
10. Type **30** in the **Length** box.
11. Click **OK**.

12. Select the top face of the model.
13. Click the **Thickness** icon on the **Part Design Modeling** toolbar.
14. Type **1** in the **Thickness** box.
15. Select **Joint Type > Intersection**.
16. Check the **Make thickness inwards** option.
17. Click **OK**.

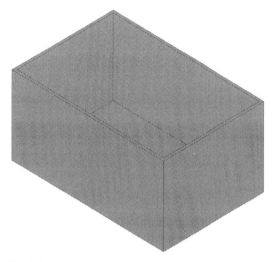

18. Select **Sheet Metal** from the **Workbenches** drop-down.
19. Press and hold the CTRL key and select the vertical edges of the model, as shown.

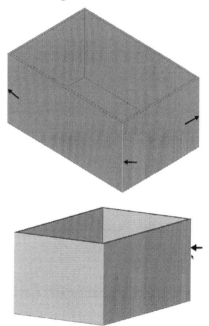

20. Click the **Make Junction** icon on the **Sheetmetal** toolbar. The selected edges are ripped opened.

21. Select the **Junction** feature from the **Combo View** panel.

22. Click the **Data** tab at the bottom of the **Combo View** panel.
23. Type **2** in the **gap** box.

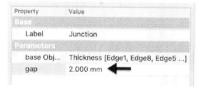

Making Bends
In this section, you will convert an edge into a bend using the Make Bend **command.**

1. Press and hold the CTRL key and select the edges on the bottom face, as shown.

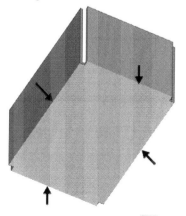

2. Click the **Make Bend** icon on the **Sheetmetal**

toolbar.

3. Click the **Model** tab on the **Combo View** panel.

4. Select **Solidbend** from the model tree.

5. On the **Properties** panel, enter **1** in the **radius** and **thickness** boxes, respectively.

Property	Value
Base	
Label	SolidBend
Parameters	
base Obj…	Junction [Edge10, Edge13, Edge7 …
radius	1.000 mm
thickness	1.000 mm

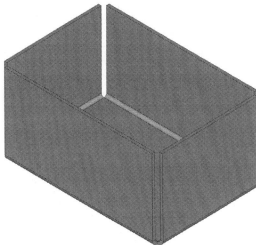

Adding Corner Relief

In this section, you will add corner reliefs to the bends. You add corner reliefs to the model to prevent deformation when the sheetmetal model is folded or unfolded.

1. Press and hold the CTRL key and select the intersecting edges of the bend, as shown.

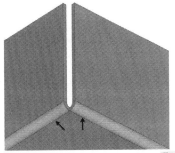

2. Click the **Corner relief** icon on the **Sheetmetal** toolbar.

3. Select **CornerRelief** from the **Model** tab of the **Combo View** panel.

4. Select **Relief Sketch > Circle**.

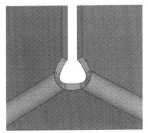

You can also select the **Circle-Scaled**, **Square**, **Square-Scaled**, or **Sketch** from the **Relief Sketch** drop-down.

Circle-Scaled

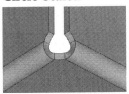

Square

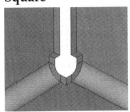

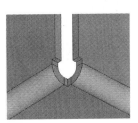

5. Likewise, add reliefs to other corners, as shown.

Making a Forming in Wall

1. Select the **Part Design** option from the **Workbenches** drop-down.

2. Click the **Create Body** 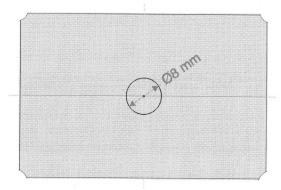 icon on the **Part Design Helper** toolbar.

3. Click the **Create Sketch** icon on the **Part Design Helper** toolbar.

4. Select the **XY_Plane001** and click **OK**.

5. Click **Sketch > View Section** on the menu bar.

6. Create a sketch, as shown.

7. Click **Close** on the **Combo View** panel.

8. Click the **Pad** icon on the **Part Design Modeling** toolbar.

9. Select **Type > Two dimensions**.

10. Type **1.5** and **-8** in the **Length** and **Taper angle** boxes, respectively.

11. Type **1.5** in the **2nd Length** box and click **OK**.

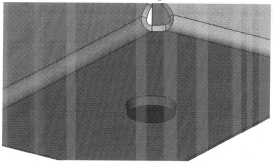

12. Click on the circular edge of the pad feature, as shown.

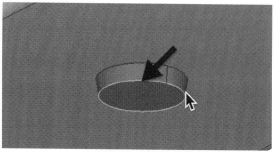

13. Click the **Fillet** icon on the **Part Design Modeling** toolbar.

14. Type **1** in the **Radius** box and click **OK**.

15. In the **Combo View** panel, right-click on the first **Body** and select **Toggle active body**.

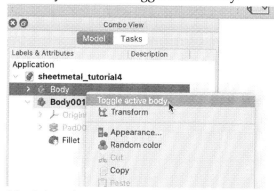

16. Select the **Sheet Metal** option from the **Workbenches** drop-down.

17. Press and hold the CTRL key and select the inner horizontal face and the top face of the newly created body.

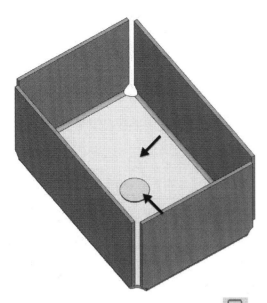

18. Click the **Make Forming in Wall** 🔲 icon on the **Part Design Modeling** toolbar. The forming is created in the wall.

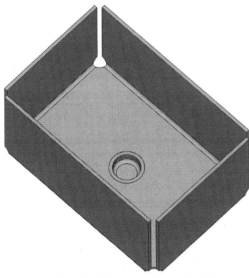

19. In the **Combo View** panel, select the **WallForming** feature.
20. In the **Properties** panel, expand the **Offset** option.

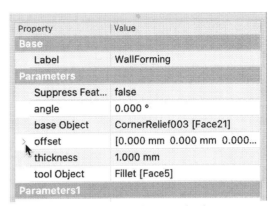

Property	Value
Base	
Label	WallForming
Parameters	
Suppress Feat...	false
angle	0.000 °
base Object	CornerRelief003 [Face21]
> offset	[0.000 mm 0.000 mm 0.000...
thickness	1.000 mm
tool Object	Fillet [Face5]
Parameters1	

21. Type **20** and **10** in the **x** and **y** boxes.

Property	Value
Base	
Label	WallForming
Parameters	
Suppress Feat...	false
angle	0.000 °
base Object	CornerRelief003 [Face21]
∨ offset	[20.000 mm 10.000 mm 0.0...
x	20.000 mm ⬅
y	10.000 mm ⬅
z	0.000 mm
thickness	1.000 mm
tool Object	Fillet [Face5]
Parameters1	
Sketch	

The wallforming feature is offset along the x and y coordinates, as shown.

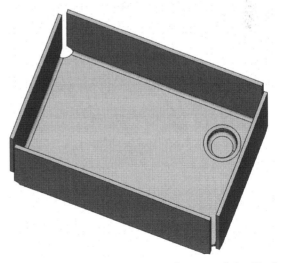

22. In the **Combo View** panel, expand the **Body001** node, and then select the **Fillet** feature.

23. Click the **View** tab and select **Visibility > true**.

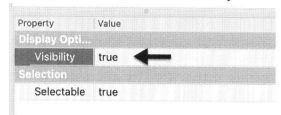

24. In the **Combo View** panel, right-click on the first **Body** and select **Toggle active body**.
25. Select the **Sheet Metal** option from the **Workbenches** drop-down.
26. Press and hold the CTRL key and select the inner horizontal face and the top face of **Body001**.

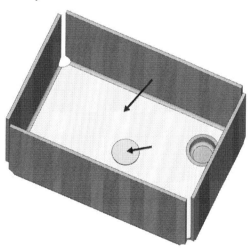

27. Click the **Make Forming in Wall** icon on the **Part Design Modeling** toolbar. The forming is created in the wall.
28. In the **Combo View** panel, select the **WallForming001** feature.

29. In the **Properties** panel, click the **Data** tab.
30. Expand the **Offset** option.
31. Type **20** and **-10** in the **x** and **y** boxes. The wall forming is offset to the new location.

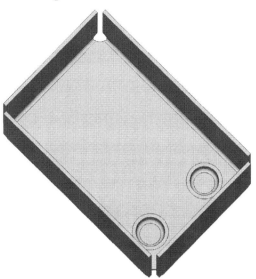

32. Likewise, create two more wall formings and offset them to new locations.

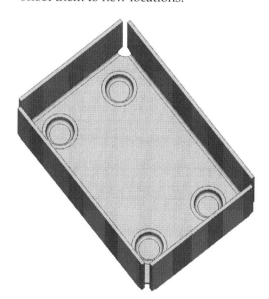

26. Save and close the file.

Chapter 8: CAM Overview

TUTORIAL 1

In this tutorial, you generate paths for the machining operations of the part shown in the figure below.

1. Download the Tutorial 1-part file of Chapter 12, and open it.
2. Select **Path** from the **Workbenches** drop-down.

3. Click **Edit > Preferences** on the menu bar.
4. Click the **General** option on the left side of the **Preferences** dialog.
5. Click the **Units** tab.
6. Select **User system > Metric small parts and CNC (mm, mm/min)**.
7. Click **OK**.

Creating the Job

1. Click the **Job** icon on the **Project Setup** toolbar.

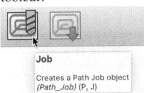

2. On the **Create Job** dialog, select the checkbox next to the Body.
3. Click **OK**.
4. On the **Job Edit** dialog, click the **Setup** tab.
5. Select **Extend Model's Bound Box** from the drop-down located at the top.
6. Type **5** in the **Ext. X** and **Ext. Y** boxes.
7. Type **50** and **2** in the first and second **Ext. Z** boxes, respectively.

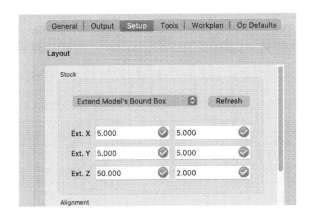

8. Click on the top-left corner of the bounding box.

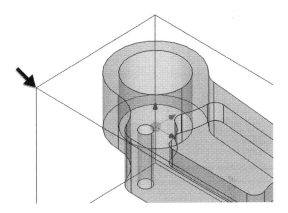

9. Click the **Set Origin** button in the **Alignment** section of the **Setup** tab of the **Job Edit** dialog.

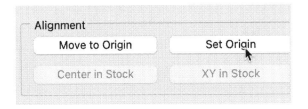

The origin is moved to the selected location, as shown.

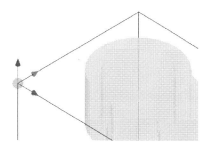

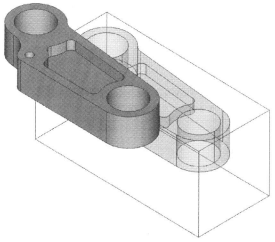

10. Click the **Output** tab on the **Job Edit** dialog.
11. Select **linuxcnc** from the **Processor** drop-down.
12. Type **Tutorial1.ngc** in the **Output file** box.
13. Click **OK**.

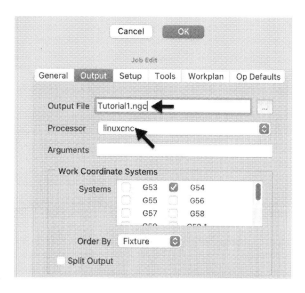

14. In the **Model** tab of the **Combo View** panel, go to **Job > Model**.
15. Press and hold the Ctrl key and select **Stock** and **Model-Body**.
16. Right-click and select **Show selection**.

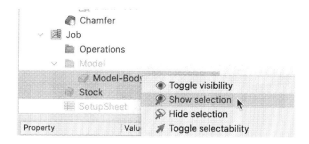

17. Right click on **Body**, and then select **Hide selection**.

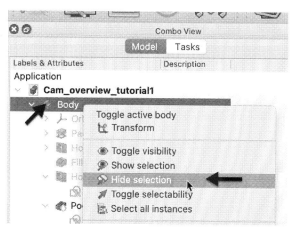

Adding Tools to the Job

Follow the steps given next to add tools in Windows version of FreeCAD 0.20.1.

1. Click the **Tool Manager i**con on the **Tool Commands** toolbar.

2. Click the **Add Tools Table** icon on the left side of the **Tools Library** dialog.

3. Click the **New Tool** button on the **Tool Library** dialog.
4. On the **Tool Editor** dialog, type **End Mill 5 mm** in the **Name** box.
5. Select **Type > EndMill**.
6. Select **Material > Carbide**.
7. Type **1** in the **Length Offset** box.
8. Type **5** and **30** in the **D** and **H** boxes, respectively.
9. Click **OK**.

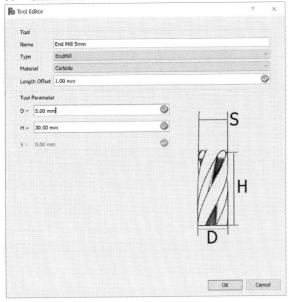

10. Click the **New Tool** button on the **Tool Library** dialog.
11. Type **Drill 5 mm** in the **Name** box.
12. Select **Type > Drill**.
13. Select the **Material > Carbide**.
14. Type **1** in the **Length Offset** box.
15. Type **5**, **15**, and **180** in the D, H, and a boxes, respectively.
16. Click **OK**.

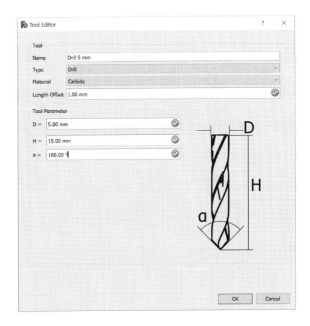

17. In the **Combo View** panel, right-click on the **Job** node and select **Edit**.
18. Click the **Tools** tab, and then click the **Add** button.
19. On the **Tools Library** dialog, select the checkboxes of the two newly created tools and click the **Create Tool Controllers** button.
20. Click **OK** to add the tools to the job.
21. Click **OK** on the **Combo View** panel.

Follow the steps given next to add tools to the Job in the Mac version of the FreeCAD 0.20.1.

1. Click the **ToolBit Dock** icon on the **Tool Commands** toolbar.
2. Press and hold the CTRL key and select the End Mill 5 mm and 5 mm Drill tools from the Tool Selector.

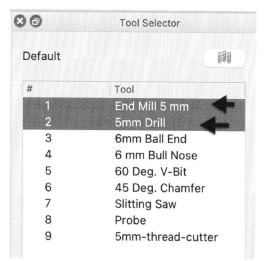

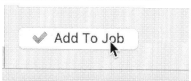

3. Click the **Add to Job** button located at the bottom of the Tool Selector.

4. Expand the **Tools** folder on the **Combo View** panel; the tool controllers are listed.

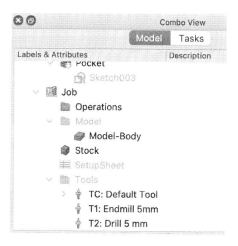

Creating the Facing Operation

1. Click the **Face** icon on the **New Operations** toolbar.

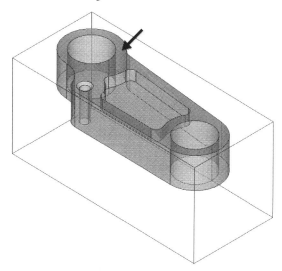

2. Select the **Endmill 5mm** tool controller from the **Choose Tool controller** dialog.

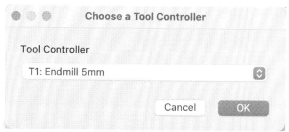

3. Expand the **Base Geometry** section on the **MillFace** dialog.

4. Select the top face of the model.

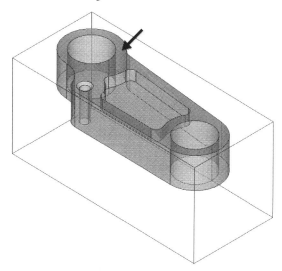

5. Click the **Add** button in the **Base Geometry** section.

6. Expand the **Depths** section on the **MillFace** dialog. Notice that the **Final Depth** value is calculated automatically.

7. Click the **Formula** icon next to the **Step Down** box.

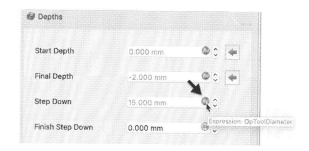

8. Type **1** in the **Formula editor** dialog.

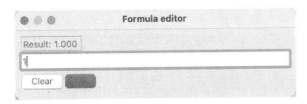

9. Click **OK**.
10. Expand the **Operation** section on the **MillFace** dialog.
11. Select **Boundary Shape > Stock**.
12. Select **Cut Mode > Conventional**.
13. Select **Pattern > Zig Zag**.
14. Leave the default values in the **Angle**, **Step Over Percent**, and **Material Allowance** boxes.
15. Click the **Apply** button located at the top of the **Tasks** tab; the preview of the toolpath appears.

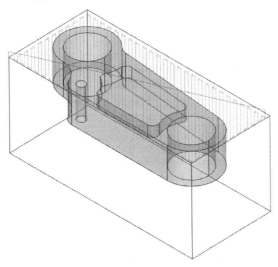

16. Click **OK** to accept the toolpath. You can also change the values on the **MillFace** dialog and click **Apply** to see the result.
17. Expand the **Operations** node in the **Model** tab of the **Combo View** panel; the **MillFace** operation is listed.

18. Place the pointer on the path and notice that arrow. It displays the direction of the path.

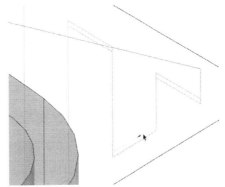

Notice the safety path. You can change the safe height and clearance using the **SetupSheet**.

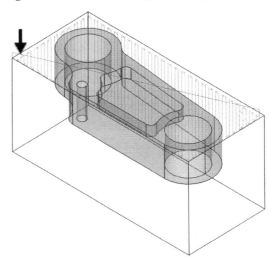

19. Select **SetupSheet** under the Job node in the **Model** tab.

You can change the **Clearance Height Offset** and **Safe Height Offset** values in the **Properties** panel.

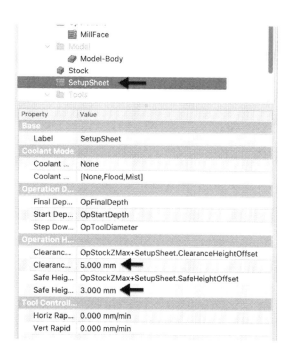

You can also define the feed of the tool.

20. Double-click on **Endmill 5mm** tool
controller under the **Job** node.

21. Type **200**, **60**, and **10000** in the **Horiz. Feed**,
Vert. Feed and **Spindle** boxes, respectively.

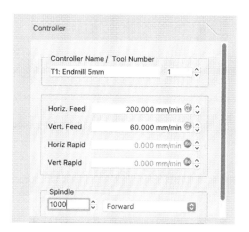

22. Click **OK**.
23. Select the **MillFace** operation from the
Model tab.
24. Click the **Toggle the Active State of the**
Operation icon on the **Tool Commands**
toolbar.

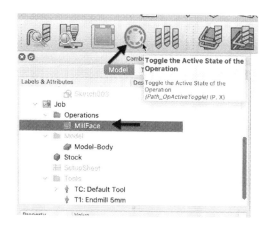

The MillFace path is hidden.

Creating the Pocket Operation

1. Select the flat face of the pocket, as shown.

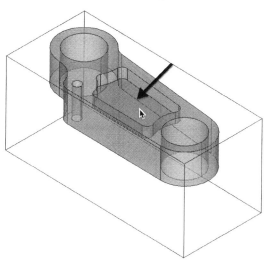

2. Click the **Pocket Shape** icon on the **New**
Operations toolbar.

3. Expand the **Depths** section.
4. Click the **Formula** icon next to the **Step**

Down box.

5. Type **1** in the **Formula editor** dialog, and then click **OK**.
6. Expand the **Operation** section.
7. Select **Endmill 5mm** from the **Tool Controller** drop-down.
8. Select **Cut Mode > Conventional**.
9. Select **Pattern > ZigZagOffset**.
10. Click **Apply** to view the path.

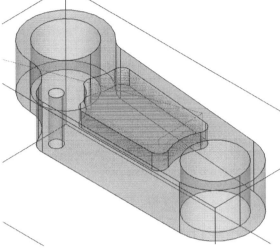

11. Click **OK**.

Creating the Drill Operation

1. Click the **Drilling** icon on the **New Operations** toolbar.

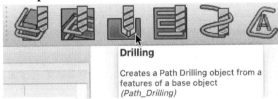

2. On the **Drilling** dialog, expand the **Base Geometry** section and notice that the all the holes are selected automatically.
3. Click the **Add** button.
4. Expand the **Depths** section and click the **Formula** icon next to the **Final Depth** box.
5. Make sure that the **Result** value is -32 on the **Formula editor** dialog.
6. Click **OK**.

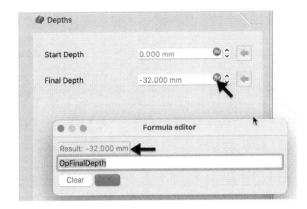

7. Expand the **Operation** section and select **Drill 5mm** from the **Tool Controller** drop-down.
8. Click **Apply** and **OK**. The drill operation is created on three holes, as shown.

Drilling Holes using the Helix Operation

1. Click the **Helix** icon on the **New Operations** toolbar.

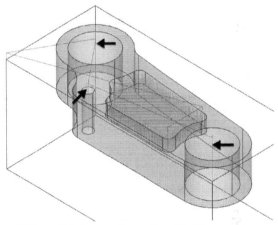

2. Select **Endmill 5mm** from the **Tool Controller** drop-down in the **Operations** section.
3. Expand the **Base Geometry** section and click the **Reset** button; all the holes available on the model are selected.
4. Expand the **Depths** section and click the **Formula** icon next to the **Step Down** box.

5. Type **2** in the **Formula editor** dialog.

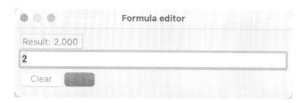

6. Click **OK**.
7. Click **Apply** and **OK**.

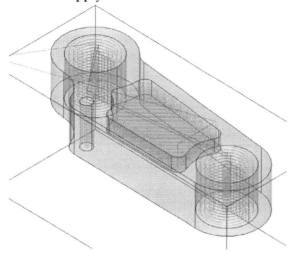

Creating the Contour Operation

1. Click the **Profile** icon on the **New Operations** toolbar.

2. Select **Endmill 5mm** from the **Tool Controller** drop-down in the **Operations** section.
3. Check the **Use Compensation** option.
4. Expand the **Depths** section.
5. Click the **Formula** icon next to the **Step Down** box.
6. Type **2** in the **Formula editor** dialog.
7. Click **OK**.
8. Click the **Formula** icon next to the **Final Depth** box.

9. Type **-32** in the **Formula editor** dialog.
10. Click **OK**.
11. Click **Apply** and **OK**.

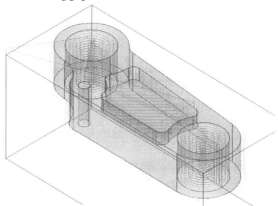

12. Select the **MillFace** operation from the **Model** tab.
13. On the **Properties** panel, go to the **Path** section, and then select **Active > True**. The MillFace path is active.

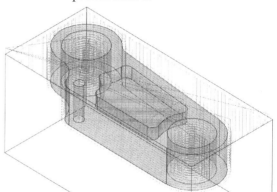

Simulating the Operations

1. Click the **CAM Simulator** icon on the **Tool Commands** toolbar.

2. Make sure that all the operations are selected on the **Path Simulator** dialog.
3. Click the **Activate/resume simulation** icon.

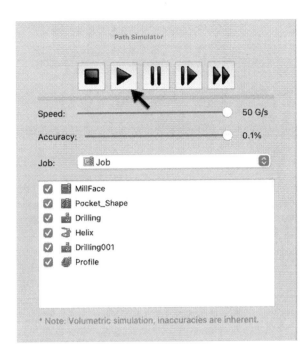

Speed: ———————○ 50 G/s

Accuracy: ———————○ 0.1%

Job: [Job]

☑ MillFace
☑ Pocket_Shape
☑ Drilling
☑ Helix
☑ Drilling001
☑ Profile

* Note: Volumetric simulation, inaccuracies are inherent.

The operations are simulated one-by-one. The final result is shown below.

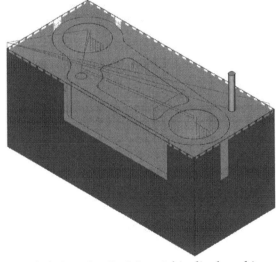

4. Click **OK**; the CutMaterial is displayed in the Model tab, as shown.

Post Processing

1. On the **Combo View** panel, expand the **Job > Operations** node.
2. Select the **MillFace** operation.

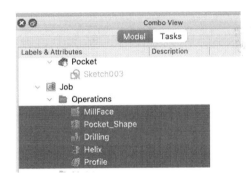

3. Click the **Inspect Path Commands** icon on the **Tool Commands** toolbar.

The G-Code is displayed on the FreeCAD dialog. If you want to learn about the G-code, please visit

https://linuxcnc.org/docs/html/gcode/g-code.html

4. Inspect the G-Code and click **Close**.
5. Likewise, inspect the G-Code of other operations.

6. Select the **Job** node from the **Model** tab.
7. Click the **Post Process** icon on the **Project Setup** toolbar.

8. Specify the location of the post-processor file and click **Save**.
9. Click **OK** on the **FreeCAD** dialog.

10. Save and close the FreeCAD file.

Made in the USA
Middletown, DE
16 August 2023

36872487R00108